Science and Technology Concepts for Middle Schools™

Light

Student Guide and Source Book

NATIONAL SCIENCE RESOURCES CENTER

The National Science Resources Center (NSRC) is operated by the Smithsonian Institution and the National Academies to improve the teaching of science in the nation's schools. The NSRC disseminates information about exemplary teaching resources, develops curriculum materials, and conducts outreach programs of leadership development and technical assistance to help school districts implement inquiry-centered science programs.

SMITHSONIAN INSTITUTION

The Smithsonian Institution was created by act of Congress in 1846 "for the increase and diffusion of knowledge. . . ." This independent federal establishment is the world's largest museum complex and is responsible for public and scholarly activities, exhibitions, and research projects nationwide and overseas. Among the objectives of the Smithsonian is the application of its unique resources to enhance elementary and secondary education.

THE NATIONAL ACADEMIES

The National Academies are nonprofit organizations that provide independent advice to the nation on matters of science, technology, and medicine. The National Academies consist of four organizations: the National Academy of Sciences, the National Academy of Engineering, the Institute of Medicine, and the National Research Council. The National Academy of Sciences was created in 1863 by a congressional charter. Under this charter, the National Research Council was established in 1916, the National Academy of Engineering in 1964, and the Institute of Medicine in 1970.

STC/MS PROJECT SPONSORS

National Science Foundation
Bristol-Myers Squibb Foundation
Dow Chemical Company
DuPont Company
Hewlett-Packard Company
The Robert Wood Johnson Foundation
Carolina Biological Supply Company

Science and Technology Concepts for Middle Schools™

Light

Student Guide and Source Book

 National Science Resources Center

THE NATIONAL ACADEMIES · Smithsonian Institution

Published by Carolina Biological Supply Company
Burlington, North Carolina

NOTICE This material is based upon work supported by the National Science Foundation under Grant No. ESI-9618091. Any opinions, findings, and conclusions or recommendations expressed in this material are those of the authors and do not necessarily reflect views of the National Science Foundation, the Smithsonian Institution, or the National Academies.

This project was supported, in part,
by the
National Science Foundation
Opinions expressed are those of the authors
and not necessarily those of the Foundation

ISBN 978-0-89278-549-0

Published by Carolina Biological Supply Company, 2700 York Road, Burlington, NC 27215.
Call toll free 1-800-334-5551.

Cover design and illustration by Max-Karl Winkler; cover photo, butterflies and flower, by Harold Dorwin, Smithsonian Institution.
Printed in the United States of America

CB792240706
♻ Printed on recycled paper.

Light

MODULE DEVELOPMENT STAFF

Developer/Writer
David Marsland

Science Advisor
Alan Migdall

Illustrator
John Norton

Editor
Jane Lawrence

Photographic Research
Betsy Thompson
Christine Hauser

Contributing Writer
Lynda DeWitt

STC/MS PROJECT STAFF

Principal Investigator
Sally Goetz Shuler, Executive Director, NSRC

Illustration Coordinator
Max-Karl Winkler

Project Director
Kitty Lou Smith

Photo Editor
Christine Hauser

Curriculum Developers
David Marsland
Henry Milne
Carol O'Donnell
Dane Toler

Graphic Designer
Heidi M. Kupke

Researcher/Writer
Carolyn Hanson

Publications Director
Heather Dittbrenner

Reader Editor
Linda Harteker

Managing Editors
Linda Griffin Kean
Dorothy Sawicki

DESIGN CONSULTATION
Isely &/or Clark Design

STC/MS Project Advisors for *Light*

Dr. David Branning, Department of Physics, University of Illinois at Urbana—Champaign

James Bickel, Teacher Instructional Service, Minneapolis

Caren Falascino, Fort Couch Middle School, Upper St. Clair

Dr. Jay Grinstead, National Institute of Standards and Technology, Optical Technology Division

Mr. Leonard Hanssen, National Institute of Standards and Technology, Optical Technology Division

Dr. Jack Hehn, Manager, Division of Education, American Institute of Physics

Mr. Paul Klein, Naval Research Laboratory

Mr. Robert Latham, Thomas Jefferson Secondary School for Science and Technology, Fairfax County, Virginia

Dr. John Layman, Professor Emeritus of Education and Physics, University of Maryland

Ms. Yvonne Mah, Montgomery County Public Schools, Maryland

Dr. Alan Migdall

Mr. Mike Isley, Carolina Biological Supply Company

Dr. Howard Yoon, Project Leader, Spectroradiometry, National Institute of Standards and Technology, Optical Technology Division

Foreword

Community leaders and state and local school officials across the country are recognizing the need to implement science education programs consistent with the National Science Education Standards as we strive to attain the important national goal of scientific literacy for all students in the 21st century. The Standards present a bold vision of science education. They identify what students at various levels should know and be able to do. They also emphasize the importance of transforming the science curriculum in a way that encourages students to engage actively in scientific inquiry—thereby developing conceptual understanding as well as problem-solving skills.

We believe that the development of effective, standards-based, inquiry-centered curriculum materials is a key step in achieving scientific literacy. The National Science Resources Center (NSRC) has responded to this challenge through the Science and Technology Concepts for Middle Schools (STC/MS) program. With the publication of the STC/MS modules, schools now have a rich set of curriculum resources for middle school students that embody scientific inquiry and hands-on learning.

Since its founding in 1985, the NSRC has made many contributions to the goal of achieving scientific literacy for all students. In addition to developing the Science and Technology for Children (STC) program—an inquiry-centered science curriculum for grades K through 6—the NSRC has been active in disseminating information on science teaching resources, in preparing school district leaders to spearhead science education reform, and in providing technical assistance to school districts. These programs have had an important impact on science education throughout the country.

The transformation of science education is a challenging task that will continue to require the kind of strategic thinking and insistence on excellence that the NSRC has demonstrated in all of its curriculum development and outreach programs. Its sponsoring organizations, the Smithsonian Institution and the National Academies, take great pride in the publication of this exciting new science program for middle schools.

J. Dennis O'Connor
Former Under Secretary for Science
Smithsonian Institution

Bruce M. Alberts
President
National Academy of Sciences

Preface

The National Science Resources Center's (NSRC) mission is to improve the learning and teaching of science for K-12 students. As an organization of two prestigious scientific institutions—the National Academies and the Smithsonian Institution—the NSRC is dedicated to the establishment of effective science programs for all students. To contribute to that goal, the NSRC has developed and published two comprehensive, research-based science curriculum programs: the Science and Technology for Children® (STC®) program for students in grades K-6, and the Science and Technology Concepts for Middle Schools™ (STC/MS™) program for students in grades 6-8.

The STC/MS curriculum project was launched in 1997. The overall design of the instructional materials and the process by which they were developed are based on a foundation of research. The STC/MS courses were informed by research on cognitive development, teaching, learning, assessment, and the culture of schools.

The STC/MS curriculum materials consist of eight courses. Through these courses, students build an understanding of important concepts in life, earth, and physical sciences and in technology; learn critical-thinking skills; and develop positive attitudes toward science and technology. The STC/MS program materials are designed to meet the challenge of the National Science Education Standards to place scientific inquiry at the core of science education programs. Specifically, the National Science Education Standards state that "...students in grades 5–8 should be provided opportunities to engage in full and partial inquiries.... With an appropriate curriculum and adequate instruction, middle school students can develop the skills of investigation and the understanding that scientific inquiry is guided by knowledge, observations, ideas, and questions." STC/MS also addresses the national technology standards published by the International Technology Education Association.

Informed by research and guided by standards, the design of the STC/MS courses addresses four critical goals:

- Use of effective student and teacher assessment strategies to improve learning and teaching
- Integration of literacy into the learning of science by giving students the lens of language to focus and clarify their thinking and activities.
- Enhanced learning using new technologies to help students visualize processes and relationships that are normally invisible or difficult to understand.
- Incorporation of strategies to actively engage parents to support the learning process.

The research and development process has included trial teaching and field-testing nationwide with geographically and ethnically diverse student populations, as well as the active involvement of the scientific and engineering communities. This process has ensured that the learning experiences contained in each module reflect current scientific thinking, and are pedagogically sound and developmentally appropriate for students.

The NSRC is grateful to the Smithsonian Institution and the National Academies for their overall project support and for sharing their scientific expertise—critical for the development of world-class products. Support for project staff and the associated work to produce and publish these materials has been made possible by the National Science Foundation, our publisher Carolina Biological Supply Company, and numerous private foundations and corporations, including Bristol-Myers Squibb Foundation, The Dow Chemical Company Foundation, DuPont, the Hewlett-Packard Company, and The Robert Wood Johnson Foundation.

The NSRC would like to acknowledge Douglas M. Lapp, former NSRC Executive Director, for his vision and leadership on the STC/MS project. The STC/MS development staff, under the direction of Kitty Lou Smith, and the publications staff, under the direction of Heather Dittbrenner, working in cooperation with Dorothy Sawicki, Managing Editor for the first four modules, and Linda Griffin Kean, Managing Editor for the second four modules, are to be commended for their creativity, dedication, and commitment to develop these excellent curriculum materials that will be used to improve the learning and teaching of middle school science in the nation's schools.

We welcome comments from students and teachers about their experiences with the STC/MS program materials and recommendations for ways the STC/MS courses can be improved.*

Sally Goetz Shuler
Executive Director
National Science Resources Center

---

*Please forward your feedback and suggestions to STC/MS Program, National Science Resources Center, Smithsonian Institution, Washington, DC 20560-0403.

Acknowledgments

The National Science Resources Center gratefully acknowledges the following individuals, schools, and school systems for their assistance with the national field-testing of *Light:*

California

Site Coordinator: Leona Lallier, El Centro Elementary School District

El Centro Elementary School District, El Centro
John Lazarcik, Teacher, Kennedy Middle School

Calexico Unified School District, Calexico
Yolanda Guerrero, Teacher, William Moreno Junior High School

Holtville Unified School District, Holtville
Richard Sanchez, Teacher, Holtville Middle School

Maryland

Montgomery County Public Schools
Yvonne Mah, Teacher, Shady Grove Middle School, Gaithersburg

Minnesota

Site Coordinator: James Bickel, Teacher Instructional Service, Minneapolis Public Schools

Minneapolis Public Schools, Minneapolis
John Roper-Batker, Teacher, Seward Montessori School
Tracey Schultz, Teacher, Franklin Middle School
Diane Weiher, Teacher, Franklin Middle School

North Carolina

Alamance-Burlington School System, Burlington
Elizabeth Thornburg, Teacher, Woodlawn Middle School, Mebane

Pennsylvania

Site Coordinator: Jim Smoyer, Allegheny Schools Science Education and Technology (ASSET), Pittsburgh

Upper Saint Clair School District, Upper Saint Clair
Nelson Earley, Teacher, Fort Couch Middle School
Caren Falascino, Teacher, Fort Couch Middle School

Northgate School District, Pittsburgh
Frank Nesko, Teacher, Northgate Junior and Senior High School

Tennessee

Site Coordinator: Jimmie Lou Lee, Center for Excellence for Research and Policy on Basic Skills, Tennessee State University, Nashville

Williamson County Schools
Barbara Duke, Teacher, Grassland Middle School, Franklin

Metro Nashville Public Schools, Nashville
Kathy Lee, Teacher, Martin Luther King Magnet School

Sumner County Schools
Shelli White, Teacher, Rucker Stewart Middle School, Gallatin

The NSRC also thanks the following individuals from Carolina Biological Supply Company for their contribution to the development of this module:

Dianne Gerlach, Director of Product Development

Bobby Mize, Department Head, Publications
Mike Isley, Product Developer
Dr. Amy Clark, Product Developer
Jennifer Manske, Publications Manager
Gary Metheny, Editor
Bruce Anliker, Designer

The NSRC appreciates the contribution of its STC/MS project evaluation consultants:

Program Evaluation Research Group (PERG), Lesley College

Sabra Lee, Researcher, PERG

Center for the Study of Testing, Evaluation, and Education Policy (CSTEEP), Boston College

Joseph Pedulla, Director, CSTEEP

The NSRC would also like to thank Eastman Kodak Company for supplying the One-Time-Use cameras.

Contents

CONTENTS

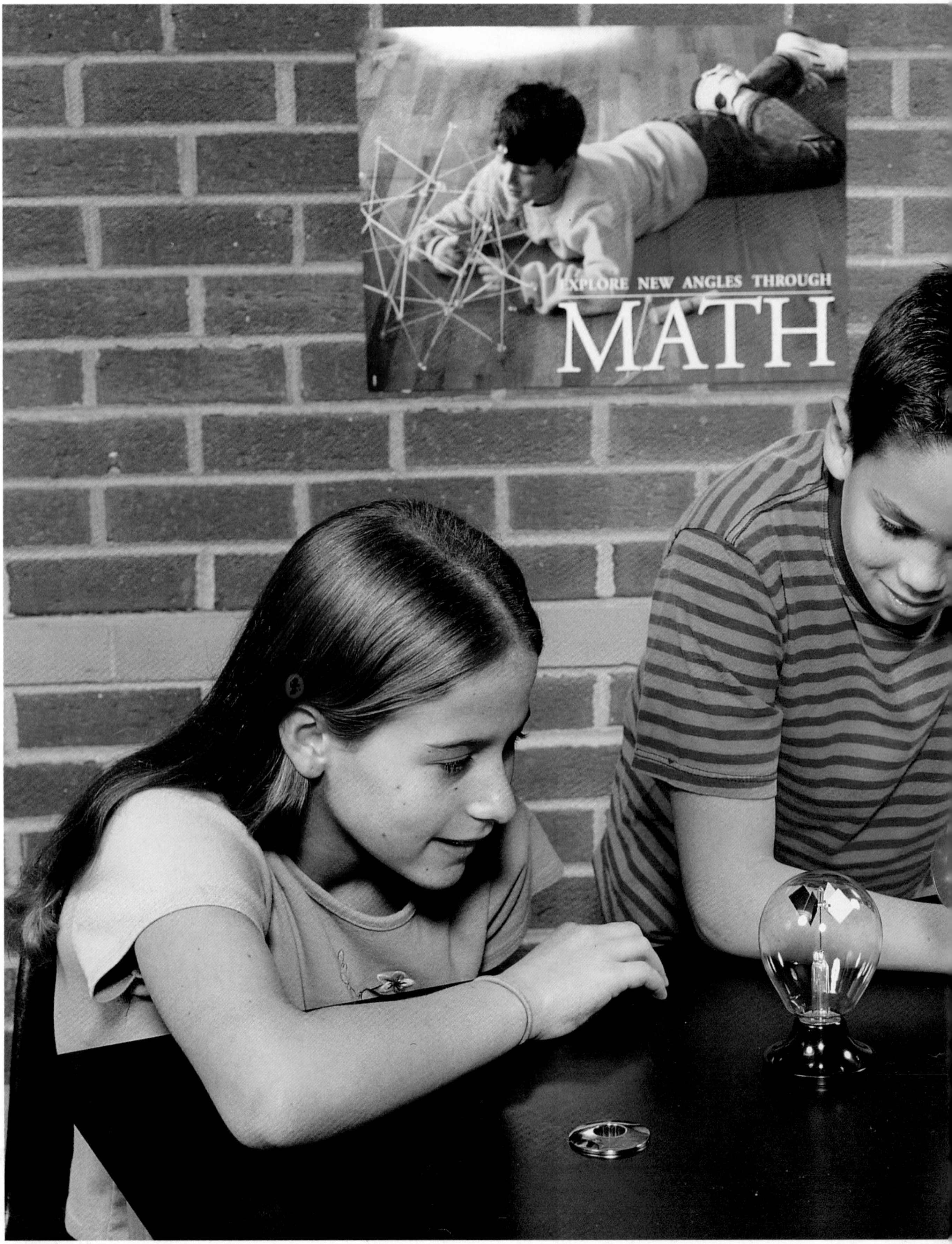
EXPLORE NEW ANGLES THROUGH
MATH

JEFF MCADAMS, PHOTOGRAPHER, COURTESY OF CAROLINA BIOLOGICAL SUPPLY COMPANY

PART 1 The Nature of Light

Thinking About Light

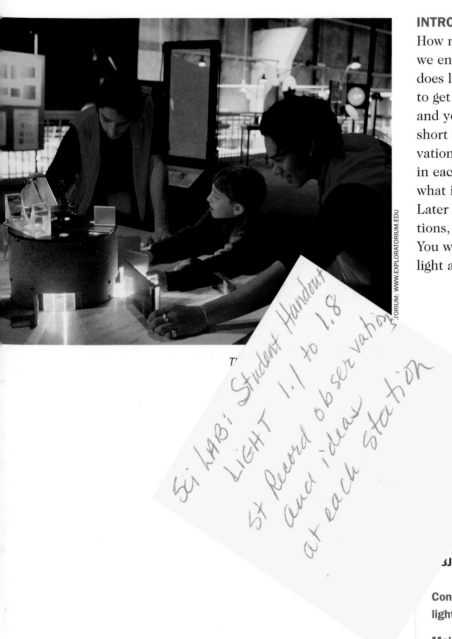

[EXPLORATORIUM: WWW.EXPLORATORIUM.EDU]

*Sci LAB: Student Handout LIGHT 1.1 to 1.8
St Record observations and ideas at each station*

INTRODUCTION

How much do you know about light? When do we encounter light? How do we use it and how does light behave? This first lesson is designed to get you thinking about these questions. You and your lab partner will conduct a series of short inquiries. You will make and record observations and discuss what you think is happening in each inquiry. If you have questions about what is happening, you will write them down. Later in the lesson, you will share your observations, ideas, and questions with your classmates. You will revisit your ideas and questions about light as you proceed through the module.

OBJECTIVES FOR THIS LESSON

Conduct a series of short inquiries about light.

Make and record observations.

Discuss your observations and ideas about what is happening.

Identify and share questions you might have about light.

Getting Started

1. Look at the nail and then stand it in the cup of water. Look at the nail in the water from a variety of different angles. What do you observe?

2. Discuss what you have observed with your group. You will be asked to share your observations with the class.

3. Record the class's observations (write or draw them) in the second column of Table 1 on Student Sheet 1.1: Thinking About Light.

4. Can you explain what is happening? Share your ideas with the class. Record some of the class's ideas in the third column of Table 1.

5. Think of some possible questions that arise from your observations. Share these questions with the class.

6. Write any questions the class has about this exercise in the fourth column of Table 1.

MATERIALS FOR LESSON 1

For you
1 copy of Student Sheet 1.1: Thinking About Light

For your group
1 transparent cup (three-fourths filled with water)
1 aluminum nail
2 index cards
1 marker

Inquiry Procedure

You are now ready to conduct the inquiries in this lesson. Just as in "Getting Started," you will discuss and record your observations, your ideas about what is happening, and your questions in Table 1 on the student sheet. Here are a few general instructions:

1. You will conduct inquiries with another student at eight different stations. The inquiries are numbered from 1.1–1.8 (or 1.1A–1.8A). Each inquiry has instructions you need to follow and questions designed to help you make observations and think about what is happening.

2. Your teacher will tell you and your partner at which station to begin.

3. Record your observations, ideas, and questions for each inquiry in the correct row of Table 1 for that inquiry.

4. When your teacher calls time, make sure you leave each inquiry as you found it before moving on to the inquiry with the next number in the sequence.

5. When you have completed all eight inquiries, return to your desk.

Inquiry 1.1
Cutlery Optics

PROCEDURE

1. Look at both sides of the spoon (see Figure 1.1).

2. What do you observe when you look at different sides of the spoon? Carefully record your observations.

3. Discuss what you think is happening with your partner. Record your ideas.

4. Record any questions you have about what you observed.

Figure 1.1 *Hold the spoon by the handle. What do you observe when you look at the inside and the outside of the spoon? Make sure you record your observations.*

Inquiry 1.2
Special Glasses

PROCEDURE

1. Put on the special glasses, and plug in the light stand (see Figure 1.2).

2. Use colored pencils and a sketch to help you describe your observations. What do you think is happening? Where do you think the colors come from?

3. Record any questions you have about what you observed.

4. Unplug the light. Return the glasses to their original position on the desk.

Figure 1.2 *Put on the special glasses and describe what you see. Have you seen something like this before?*

Inquiry 1.3
Lamp Light

PROCEDURE

1. Slowly slide the dimmer switch up and down (see Figure 1.3). Record your observations.

2. What do you think is happening? Discuss your ideas with your partner before you write them down.

3. Record any questions you have about what you observed.

4. Switch off the lamp.

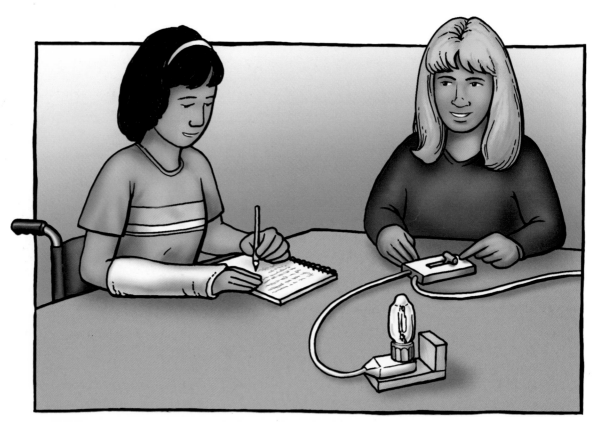

Figure 1.3 *Can you describe what happens inside the lightbulb when you slide the dimmer switch up and down? (Note: The dimmer switch you are using may differ slightly from the one shown.)*

Inquiry 1.4
The Radiometer

PROCEDURE

1. Switch on the flashlight. Point the beam at the radiometer. (See Figure 1.4.)

2. Record what you observe. What effect does moving the flashlight nearer to and farther from the radiometer have on the radiometer?

3. Record what you think is happening.

4. Record any questions you have about what you observed.

Figure 1.4 *What effect does moving the flashlight nearer to and farther from the radiometer have on the radiometer?*

Inquiry 1.5
Colored Lightbulbs

PROCEDURE

1. Switch on the power strip with the three colored lightbulbs.

2. Hold the piece of paper above the lightbulbs, and look at the paper (see Figure 1.5).

3. Being careful not to touch the lightbulbs, place one hand between the paper and the lightbulbs.

4. Describe what you see on the paper.

5. Try to explain to your partner what you observe. Record your ideas, explanations, and any questions you have about this inquiry.

6. Switch off the strip of lightbulbs.

Figure 1.5 *Hold the paper above the colored lightbulbs.*

Inquiry 1.6
Looking Behind

PROCEDURE

1. Hold the mirror in front of you, while your partner stands behind you. Move the mirror so that you can see your partner. Record your observations.

2. Try drawing a sketch in the third column of Table 1 that explains how you can see your partner.

3. Record any questions you have about what you observed.

Inquiry 1.7
Missing Flesh

PROCEDURE

1. You and your partner can do this experiment at the same time. Pick up a tube and hold it to your right eye. Look down the tube.

2. Position your left hand halfway down the side of the tube with the palm facing you (see Figure 1.6).

3. Keeping both eyes open, describe what you see to your partner. Record your observations.

4. Is there any missing flesh? Discuss with your partner what is really happening. Record your ideas and questions.

Figure 1.6 *Pick up a tube and hold it to your right eye. Place your left hand in the position shown.*

Inquiry 1.8
Looking Through an Object

PROCEDURE

1. Examine the object you have been given. Draw the object in the second column of Table 1. Write a short description of the object under your drawing. Describe what you observe when you look through the object at the print on this page (as shown in Figure 1.7). Now look at more distant things, such as the other side of the room or the scene outside the window.

2. Discuss with your partner how the object produces these effects. Record your ideas and explanations.

3. Record any questions you have about what you observed.

Figure 1.7 *Look through the object to view the print and pictures on this page.*

REFLECTING ON WHAT YOU'VE DONE

1. Share your observations, ideas, and explanations with the other pair of students in your group. Compare the questions you have generated.

2. From these questions, select the two questions that your group members agree they would most like to be able to answer.

3. Work with your group to improve the wording of these two questions.

   A. Write the questions on your student sheet. Be sure to indicate which inquiry each question came from.

4. Your teacher will give you two index cards. Use the marker to write one question on each card. Write clearly and include the number of the inquiry your question relates to at the top left corner of the card (see Figure 1.8).

5. Your teacher will lead a review of the class's observations, ideas, and questions. Here are some things you might like to think about during this review.

   Have some groups asked similar questions? Are some versions of these questions better than others?

   Can the questions be placed into groups or topics? Can you suggest names for these topics?

Figure 1.8 *Discuss with your group your questions for the inquiries. Identify your group's two questions and write one question on each of the index cards as shown.*

Using and Studying Light

Light is an important part of our lives. Even so, most of the time we take it for granted. Few people consider where light comes from, how it is detected, or how it behaves. But light is present almost all of the time. Even at night, we can see shadows indicating that there is light—perhaps from the stars or the Moon. Only in the darkest room or in a deep cave can there be a complete lack of light. However, humans have found ways to bring light into dark places, for example, by using fire, flashlights, and other light sources.

Sensing Light

Light is so important to living things that almost all organisms can detect light in some way. For instance, plants grow in such a way as to bend toward light. Microbes sometimes move either toward or away from light.

Most animals have special light detectors. Humans have two light detectors: their eyes. Without light we couldn't use one of our five senses—sight. We would have no way to see the world around us. No one could enjoy the work of great painters who express themselves using shape and color.

Without light we couldn't use some types of technology to learn, entertain, and communicate. Photographers used light to make images on light-sensitive film to produce the pictures you see in this book. Movies, television shows, and computer games use light to entertain us. People even listen to music by using laser light in CD players. Make a phone call or send an e-mail or instant message to your friends, and chances are you are communicating through tiny glass fiber-optic cables that carry your message as pulses of light.

Light can be used to entertain. At a rock concert, loud music and flashing lights create an atmosphere of fun and excitement.

© NEAL PRESTON/CORBIS

© GARY CARTER/VISUALS UNLIMITED

These flowers open during the daytime and close at night. To do this, the plant must have some way to detect light. How does the plant detect light? How do we detect light?

Humans have used fire for hundreds of thousands of years to provide light and heat. This San nomad from southern Africa coaxes a cooking fire by blowing on burning grass and twigs. How does a fire like this produce light?

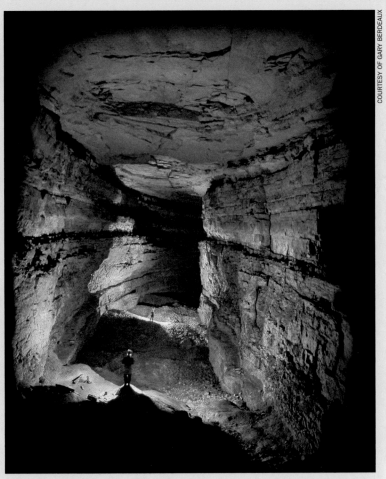

Without a light source, these cavers would see nothing of this immense cavern.

Light and Science

As scientists work to understand the natural world, they use light to make observations. They may use special instruments that use light to assist them in this work. For example, astronomers use telescopes to observe the night sky. They use other instruments to analyze light from distant stars and galaxies to determine the substances from which they are composed. Biologists use microscopes to uncover the hidden workings of cells. But before scientists could construct these modern scientific tools, they had to learn about the nature and behavior of light. This study of light is called optics.

Humans' interest in optics can be traced back thousands of years—even before recorded history. The first book about optics was written more than two thousand years ago. Early questions about light may have included the following: Why can reflections be seen on the surface of water? Why does sunlight produce fire when it passes through specially shaped polished crystals? Perhaps the most difficult question may have been, What is light? This question continues to preoccupy even modern scientists. ☐

Our knowledge of optics has enabled us to build giant telescopes that allow us to see deep into the universe. This telescope sits atop Kitt Peak in Arizona. A knowledge of optics also allows us to look at the world of the very small— the microscopic.

Light Pioneers

For thousands of years scientists and artists have studied light.

Euclid (330 B.C.–260 B.C.), a Greek mathematician and physicist, probably wrote the first book about optics two thousand years ago.

Leonardo da Vinci (1452–1519) had one of the most curious minds in history. This Italian artist, scientist, and engineer observed light and asked himself many questions about it. He then applied the results of his inquiries into the nature of light, reflections, and shadows to his great works of art.

The scientist Albert Einstein (1879–1955) is perhaps the most famous of the many scientists who have contributed over the past hundred years to a better understanding of the nature of light.

The Sun:
A SOURCE OF LIGHT, MYTH, AND TRADITION

Each dawn, not far from the shores of the Bay of Bengal, India, the first rays of the rising Sun strike the 13th–century sun temple of Konark. The temple was built in the form of a giant 24–wheeled chariot drawn by seven horses to honor the sun god Surya. According to legend, only such a magnificent chariot was fit to carry Surya across the sky in his dawn-to-dusk journey.

The Konark temple in India was built in the form of a chariot. In legend, this horse-drawn chariot carries the sun god Surya across the sky.

A wheel from a temple chariot fit for a sun god

Six hours later, the Sun's early morning rays touch the stones of Stonehenge in England. Ancient Britons built this giant astronomical calendar and center for sun worship four thousand years ago. Throughout history, people from all over the world have worshipped the Sun, our closest star. They have recognized it as the source of the light and heat so essential for life. No wonder many cultures gave the Sun the status of a god.

The early Egyptians built elaborate temples to their sun gods, Re and Aton. The ancient Greeks also had sun gods—first Helios and then Apollo. The Greeks also explained the Sun's apparent movement across the sky in terms of a golden chariot light for both humans and gods.

In addition to worshipping sun gods, some peoples—like the Japanese—believed that their rulers were descended from sun gods.

Ancient Britons built Stonehenge as an astronomical calendar and a place of sun worship. Some of its giant stones were dragged over 160 kilometers (100 miles) to the site. The stones are arranged so that on a midsummer's day the rays of the rising Sun shine into the center of the monument.

Celebrating the Sun

Have you ever thought about where the word "Sunday" came from? In A.D. 313, the Roman emperor Constantine became a Christian. He then changed the day for worshipping the Roman sun god, Sol Victis, into a day for worship for Christians—*Sun*day. Even celebrations on December 25 began as a day of sun worship. Originally celebrated as the Feast of Sun in India, this celebration became Christmas in the West.

Celebration of the Sun also was common among the early inhabitants of the Americas. The Aztecs, Incas, and Mayans recognized the Sun as a deity. They staged elaborate rituals and sacrifices in temples created specially for these gods.

Some of the native peoples of the North American plains still hold a renewal ceremony in spring or early summer, called the Sun Dance. This four-day event of rituals and dances celebrates the Sun and the forces of nature.

Just as the Statue of Liberty stands at the gateway to New York, so a statue of the sun god Helios guarded the ancient harbor of Rhodes, a Greek island. The statue, known as the Colossus of Rhodes, is considered one of the Seven Wonders of the Ancient World. It stood more than 30 meters tall and was made from bronze melted down from the weapons of a defeated enemy.

The Sun has long been important to the culture and traditions of the world's peoples. Modern scientists explain the Sun, not as a god, but as a giant ball of gas—about 1,400,000 kilometers in diameter—that releases light and heat from the nuclear reactions that occur inside it. □

EXERCISE

Use books, CD-ROMs, or the Internet to research examples of sun worship other than the ones mentioned in the reader. Write a paragraph about an example you find.

This Aztec calendar stone, or sun stone, weighs almost 25 tons. In 1497, the stone was dedicated to the Aztec's main deity—the Sun. The stone's many carvings bear witness to the great cultural significance of the Sun to the Aztec culture.

Until 1945, the Japanese royal family traced its descent from the sun goddess Amaterasu Omikami (here being released from a cave), a goddess of one of Japan's oldest religions, Shinto.

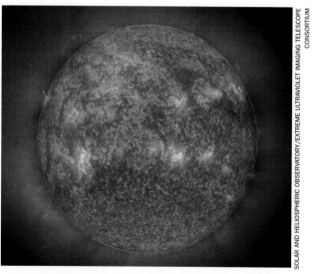

The surface of the Sun is very hot and releases a lot of light. Are light and heat related?

Where Does Light Come From?

We use artificial light sources to help us to see. How do light sources like lamps produce light? Where does light come from?

CORBIS/ROYALTY-FREE

INTRODUCTION

Everyone knows that light exists. But what is light? Where does light come from, and how is it made? From your own observations, you know that some objects make light. The most important of these is the Sun. Do you know how the Sun and other objects make light? In this lesson, you will try to answer some of these questions. You will identify different sources of light and then conduct an inquiry to examine two of these sources—a flashlight and a lit candle—in more detail. You will discuss the nature of light and some processes by which it is made.

OBJECTIVES FOR THIS LESSON

Share your ideas on the nature of light.

Identify different sources of light.

Investigate some sources of light.

Discuss light as a form of energy.

Discuss a range of energy transformations.

Investigate and discuss the transformation of light into other forms of energy.

Getting Started

1. In your science notebook, record your own ideas about the following questions:

A. What do you think light is?

B. What do you think light is not?

C. Where does the light in the classroom come from?

2. Be prepared to share your ideas with the class.

MATERIALS FOR LESSON 2

For you
1 copy of Student Sheet 2.2: How Is Light Produced?
1 pair of safety goggles

For you and your lab partner
1 flashlight
2 D-cell batteries
1 petri dish (lid or base)
1 tea candle

Inquiry 2.1
Identifying Sources of Light

PROCEDURE

1. You have identified a source, or some sources, of light within your classroom. Working with your group, think of other sources of light. List those sources in your notebook.

2. Your teacher will ask you to contribute to a class brainstorm on different light sources. Your teacher will record the class's ideas on a concept map. As the concept map builds up, record it in your notebook.

Inquiry 2.2
How Is Light Produced?

PROCEDURE

1. One member of your group should collect a plastic box of materials. Divide the materials between the pairs in your group. Record your responses on Student Sheet 2.2: How Is Light Produced?

2. Working with your partner, examine the flashlight (see Figure 2.1). You may take it apart if you wish, but be careful not to break it. Do not dismantle the switch. As you examine the flashlight, answer the following questions. Use words and/or diagrams to record your results and ideas.

SAFETY TIP

Put on your safety goggles before proceeding with the inquiry.

Figure 2.1 *Try to find out how a flashlight produces light.*

A. Exactly where does the flashlight release its light?

B. Where does this light come from?

C. Where does the light go?

D. Is anything produced in addition to light?

E. Try to explain how the flashlight makes light.

3. Reassemble the flashlight. Check to see that it works.

4. Place the candle on the petri dish. Use a match (or ask your teacher) to ignite the candle. Observe what happens as the match is struck and ignites the candle.

5. Think about the following questions, and then answer them on the student sheet:

F. What was produced when you struck the match?

G. Where did what was produced when you struck the match come from?

H. How does the candle make light?

I. Is anything else produced in addition to light?

J. What happens to the candle as it makes light?

6. Extinguish your candle. Return all the materials to the plastic box.

SAFETY TIP

Your teacher may give you a book of matches to use to light the candle. Use caution when lighting the match. Always strike a match away from you and other students, and be very careful not to burn your fingers. Do not play with the matches. Avoid breathing in the fumes from the match.

REFLECTING ON WHAT YOU'VE DONE

1. Read "Transforming Energy."

2. Discuss A–C with your group. Record your responses on the student sheet.

A. Was light stored in any of the items you examined?

B. What had to happen for light to be produced?

C. Write down the energy transformations taking place in the flashlight and the candle.

3. Look at the scene shown in Figure 2.2. (This is the same scene as the "Where's the Energy?" picture on your student sheet.)

D. Work with the class to identify any forms of energy you see on the picture. Mark and write the names of these forms of energy on or around the edge of the picture on your student sheet.

E. Under the picture write down any examples of energy transformations you see happening in the picture (one example is provided under E on the student sheet). Can you identify those that involve light energy?

WHERE'S THE ENERGY?

Figure 2.2 *Identify the forms of energy you see in this scene. Mark and write the names of these forms of energy on or around the edge of the picture on your student sheet.*

4. If light is a form of energy, it should be possible to transform this energy into other forms. Watch as your teacher shows you two examples of such a transformation. Try to decide what energy transformations are taking place (see Figures 2.3 and 2.4).

F. Record your ideas on the student sheet.

G. Write a short paragraph outlining the evidence that light is a form of energy.

5. Look at the question bank cards the class generated in Lesson 1. Can you answer any of these using what you have discovered during this lesson?

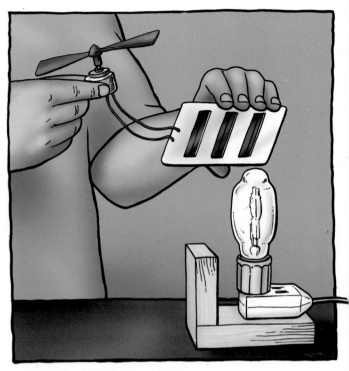

Figure 2.3 *What happens to the motor when light strikes the solar panel? What energy transformations are involved?*

Figure 2.4 *What happens when a flashlight is shone at the radiometer? What energy transformations are involved?*

TRANSFORMING ENERGY

Different light sources make light in different ways. But all light sources have something in common. They produce light as a result of energy transformations. Energy can take many forms. (Light is just one form of energy. Heat and electrical energy, movement energy, and chemical energy—stored in food or fuel—are also forms of energy. All forms of energy can do work—they can make things move.)

Energy can also be transformed from one form of energy into another form. For example, switching on the lights in your classroom allows electrical energy to enter the fluorescent tubes where some of this electrical energy is transformed into light.

When an energy transformation takes place, usually more than one form of energy is produced. Switching on the classroom lights releases light energy. But, if you touch the lit fluorescent tubes, you will also notice it is slightly warm. Heat is nearly always one of the forms of energy released during an energy transformation. The energy transformation occurring inside the tube could be expressed as follows:

Electrical energy → light and heat

Was there any evidence that heat was released during the energy transformations you observed in the flashlight, match, or candle?

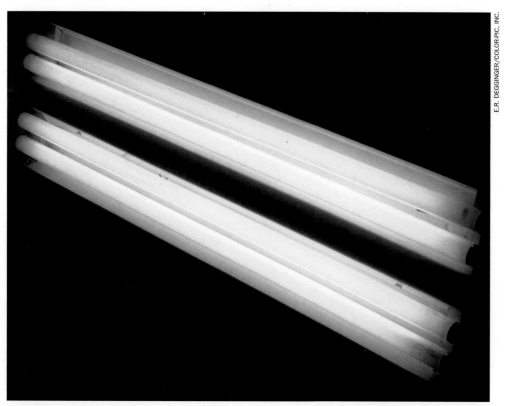

In a fluorescent tube, electrical energy passes into mercury vapor inside the tube and excites the mercury vapor. The excited vapor makes the white coating on the inside of the tube glow.

SOURCES OF LIGHT

Light sources—objects that make their own light, such as lightbulbs, the Sun, or candles—are said to be luminous. Some examples of luminous objects are shown here. Can you think of others?

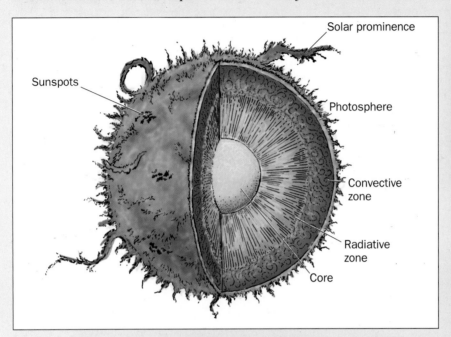

The Sun is a giant ball of gas, mainly hydrogen and helium, about 1,400,000 kilometers in diameter. Light and heat are released from the surface layer of the Sun. Inside the Sun, nuclear reactions—similar to those that occur in hydrogen bombs—release energy. The temperature in the Sun's interior is about 15,000,000 degrees Celsius (°C) (27,000,000 degrees Fahrenheit (°F)). The glowing surface of the Sun (called the photosphere) is much cooler, about 5600 °C (10,000 °F)!

JEFF MCADAMS, PHOTOGRAPHER, COURTESY OF CAROLINA BIOLOGICAL SUPPLY COMPANY

Light-emitting diodes (LEDs)—like the ones that make up the numbers in this clock—produce light from electrical energy. Because they make almost no heat, they are much more efficient at producing light than ordinary lightbulbs.

ADAM BLOCK/NATIONAL OPTICAL ASTRONOMY OBSERVATORY/ASSOCIATION OF UNIVERSITIES FOR RESEARCH IN ASTRONOMY/NATIONAL SCIENCE FOUNDATION

Lightning is produced when static electricity in clouds discharges and produces a spark. This spark is so hot that it superheats the air, causing the air to expand explosively and make thunder.

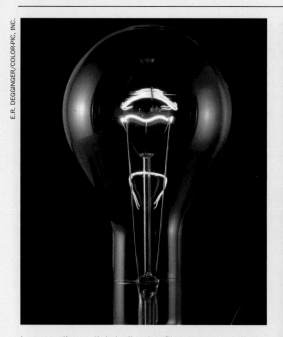

In an ordinary lightbulb, the filament—usually a piece of thin tungsten—glows when electrical energy passes through it. The filament does not burn up because it is enclosed in a glass bulb containing a non-reactive gas such as argon. In addition to light, these lightbulbs produce quite a lot of waste heat—heat that is not used. This wasted heat means these lightbulbs are not energy efficient. Fluorescent lightbulbs, which produce far less waste heat, are more energy efficient.

In glow sticks, a chemical reaction produces light, but not much heat. When the stick is bent, a glass vial inside breaks. This allows the reactants to mix. The process of producing light by this type of chemical reaction is called chemoluminescence. Unlike fire, it produces very little heat.

Fires, candles, and oil lamps release light when the fuel in them reacts with oxygen. Heat and light are produced in this chemical reaction.

In this laser, light is produced when a flash of light is used to excite atoms inside a special tube in the laser. The excited atoms produce an intense beam of single-colored light. Laser light has special properties that make it a very useful light source. You'll learn more about lasers later in the module.

L I F E
LIGHT

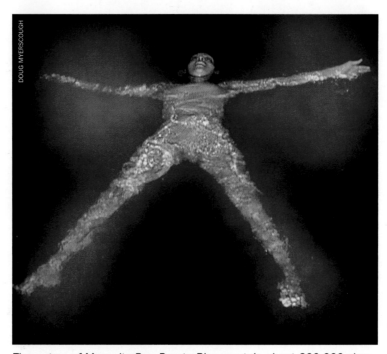

DOUG MYERSCOUGH

The waters of Mosquito Bay, Puerto Rico, contain about 200,000 glowing microbes per liter. When disturbed, as by this swimmer, they release a blue light. Sadly, this glowing performance is endangered by pollution.

Many kilometers down—in the deepest parts of the oceans—there is no sunlight. Down here in the darkness, thousands of species of organisms thrive, from single-celled microbes to giant worms and squid. Water covers much of the Earth. A huge volume of water makes up the oceans and seas. So it is not surprising that this is where you will find most of Earth's living things.

Most of this water lies in darkness. But some organisms living down here have eyes. Why have eyes if there is no light to see by? While no sunlight reaches these depths, there is light.

Many marine organisms make their own light by a process called bioluminescence—"life light." They use this light to communicate with their own species or, in some cases, as a lure to capture their prey.

For example, the flashlight fish has glowing body parts! Under its eyes are pockets that contain bioluminescent microbes (bacteria). These bacteria make light all the time, but the fish hides these glowing pockets under a movable flap of skin. When the fish wants to reveal its lights, it simply moves the flap.

But how do organisms make light? They don't

The flashlight fish has lights below its eyes. It makes light with the help of bioluminescent bacteria.

Fireflies use chemical reactions within their cells to transform chemical energy from food to light energy.

use lightbulbs, but they do have something in common with flashlights. In a flashlight, part of the chemical energy in the batteries is transformed (via electrical energy) in the lightbulb to light and heat energy. Bioluminescent organisms also transform chemical energy into light. They use special enzymes—chemicals that speed up the chemical reaction—in this process. These enzymes cause a chemical called luciferin to react with oxygen. Light energy is released during this reaction.

Bioluminescence is very common in marine organisms. Many fish and squid glow. So do some microscopic organisms that float in the water. These are sometimes present in such large numbers that they can make a whole sea glow. For example, Mosquito Bay, Puerto Rico, is famous for its nightly performance of bioluminescence.

Organisms living in the depths of the oceans are not the only species that make their own light. Some nonmarine organisms also make light. Have you ever seen fireflies or lightning bugs? They use bioluminescence to communicate

with each other. Try communicating with them on a warm summer's evening by using a flashlight. You may be surprised how many will reply to a short flash of light!

Go for a nighttime walk in the woods and you may observe rotting trees that glow in the dark. Glowing fungi inhabit the trees. Why do they glow? Perhaps to attract insects that can spread their spores.

Keep your eyes open. You may see other organisms glow. □

How Does Light Travel?

The Sun provides the light that illuminates our planet. Why does the space between Earth and the Sun look so dark?

NATIONAL AERONAUTICS AND SPACE ADMINISTRATION/JOHNSON SPACE CENTER

INTRODUCTION

In the previous lesson, you discussed light as being a type of energy. You discovered that light is made as a result of energy transformations. For example, in the lightbulb of the flashlight, electrical energy was transformed into light energy. Once light energy is produced, where does it go and how does it get there? In this lesson, you will observe light as it travels through and strikes different substances. You also will discuss how fast light travels.

OBJECTIVES FOR THIS LESSON

Try to detect light as it travels through air and water.

Determine how light behaves as it travels.

Discuss how to determine the speed of light.

Getting Started

1. One member of your group should collect the plastic box of materials. Remove a flashlight from the plastic box of materials.

2. Shine the flashlight toward the wall. Answer the following questions on Student Sheet 3.1: Looking at How Light Travels:

A. Does light from the flashlight reach the wall?

B. How do you know?

C. Look at Figure 3.1. Where is light from the flashlight? Draw on the picture on the student sheet to show where you could find light from the flashlight.

D. Could you see light from the flashlight between the flashlight and the wall?

E. If not, how do you know it is there? (How could you detect it?)

MATERIALS FOR LESSON 3

For you
1 copy of Student Sheet 3.1: Looking at How Light Travels

For you and your lab partner
1 flashlight
2 D-cell batteries
1 plastic soda bottle
1 length of rubber tubing
1 dropping bottle

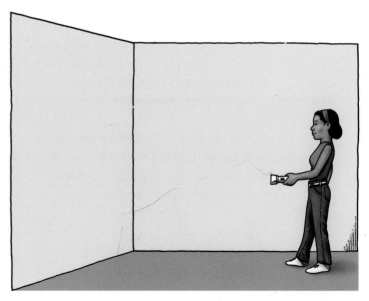

Figure 3.1 *This flashlight is switched on. Where can you find the light it is producing?*

Inquiry 3.1
Looking at How Light Travels

PROCEDURE

1. Divide the remaining materials between the pairs in your group. Use the plastic bottle and water to determine whether light travels through water. Answer the following questions on the student sheet:

A. How did you detect light on the side of the bottle opposite the flashlight?

B. Could you see light from the flashlight as it traveled through the water?

C. If you think light was passing through the water, but was invisible, how could you make it visible?

2. Test one of the suggestions from the class discussion.

D. Draw a labeled picture on the student sheet showing what you observed. Accurately describe the shape and the edges of the beam.

3. From what you have seen, do you think light travels in straight lines? Devise an experiment to test your hypothesis using the apparatus in your plastic box. Conduct your experiment.

E. Use the outline in Table 1 on the student sheet to help you describe in words and diagrams the experiment you designed and what you discovered.

REFLECTING ON WHAT YOU'VE DONE

1. You have shown that light travels through air in straight lines. How fast does it go? Discuss with your group how you could determine the speed of light. Here are some questions to think about—

What would you need to measure?

How would you make these measurements?

How accurate would your measurements need to be?

2. Participate in a class discussion on this topic.

3. Think about the points listed below. Discuss them with other students.

Does light travel through air and water?

What do you need to do to detect light?

What evidence did you gather that suggests that light travels in straight lines?

How fast does light travel?

A. Use these points to help you write a paragraph on the student sheet summarizing what you have discovered and discussed during this lesson.

Racing To Find the SPEED of Light

Light travels so fast that our eyes can't detect its movement. In the past, some people thought light traveled instantly from one place to another. Others thought light had a very fast, but finite speed—a specific speed that could somehow be measured. How do you measure such a fast speed? Think about it.

Galileo's Glimmer

Galileo, the famous 17th-century scientist, asked just that question. And he had a plan to answer it. Galileo's plan involved two lanterns, a timing device, and a willing assistant. The assistant had to be willing—his job was to walk many kilometers and hike up a steep hill carrying one of the lanterns and the timing device.

Once on top of the hill, the assistant waited until dark. He covered the lantern so no light could be seen from it, and carefully lit it. Meanwhile, a nicely rested Galileo looked toward the hill and waited. He too had a lit, covered lantern. The assistant started the timer and uncovered his lantern. As soon as Galileo saw the light, he pulled the cover off his lantern. The assistant saw the distant glimmer. He tried to measure the time it had taken for the light to travel to Galileo and back to him. Unfortunately, the light had traveled too quickly for the timer to make an accurate measurement.

Galileo's method for determining the speed of light seemed like a good idea—but it was a failure. However, Galileo did learn something. He discovered that the speed of light was very fast. So fast that it could not be measured over such a short distance using such a simple timing device.

Who is this stranger with the hidden lantern? What was his role in trying to determine the speed of light?

Roemer and the Orbit of Io

If you can't make a better timer, why not increase the distance? That's a good idea, but a huge distance would be needed—a distance on an astronomical scale. Astronomer Olas Roemer took up this challenge.

Roemer was studying Io, a moon that orbits Jupiter once every 1.76 days. He thought that he could use Io to calculate the speed of light. He knew that moons orbit planets at about the same speed regardless of the time of year. Why, he asked himself, did Io sometimes appear to be in the wrong position? At times, Io appeared to be ahead or behind its predicted position in orbit by up to 10 minutes. Roemer noticed that Io was ahead of schedule when Jupiter (with its orbiting moon Io) was near Earth and behind schedule when Jupiter was farther away.

Could the speed of the light reflected from Io to Earth have something to do with this mystery? Roemer realized that the difference in schedule could be explained if light traveled at a specific, rather than at an infinite, speed. If light traveled at a specific speed, the farther the light had to travel, the longer it would take it to reach a destination. He calculated the change in distance when Io was farthest away from Earth and divided it by the change in time from Io's predicted position. Presto! Roemer had calculated the speed of light as 220,000,000 meters per second.

The Final Figure

Roemer's calculation was pretty close, but scientists were determined to get a more accurate measurement. Many more attempts to determine the speed of light were made. The honor for the first truly accurate measurement went to the American physicist Albert Michelson. Like Galileo and Roemer, Michelson realized that to accurately measure the speed of light he needed to precisely measure the time it took light to travel a long distance. He used a specially designed apparatus with two mirrors that

were 35 kilometers apart. Using a very accurate clock, he measured the speed of light at 299,799,600 meters per second. Close, but not close enough for some scientists.

The most recent speed for light is 299,792,458 meters per second. This measurement was made using very precise atomic clocks to calculate the time it takes for light to travel over very accurately measured distances. Science has come a long way since Galileo's experiment with lanterns and a timer! ❑

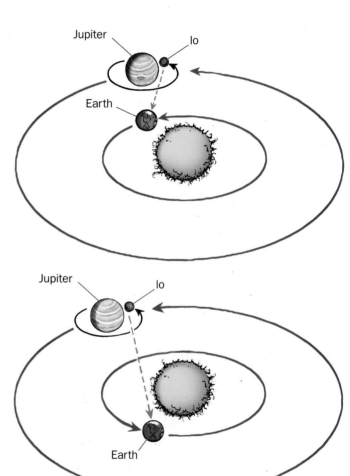

Note: Bodies and orbits are not to scale.

The farther away Jupiter and its moons are from Earth, the longer it takes light reflected from them to reach us. Roemer realized that apparent variations in the orbit time of one of Jupiter's moons and the difference in distance between it and Earth could be used to calculate the speed of light.

How did Io, a moon orbiting Jupiter, contribute to our knowledge of the speed of light?

Light Speedsters

All these scientists attempted to find the speed of light. The accuracy of their results for the speed of light depended on their ability to design experiments and build apparatus that would accurately measure time and distance.

Galileo (1564–1642) tried unsuccessfully to measure the speed of light with lanterns and a timing device.

Olas Roemer (1644–1710) used astro-nomical distances to calculate the speed of light.

Arnand Fizeau (1819–1896) designed an apparatus that used rotating mir-rors and a distance of 9 kilometers to make a more accurate measurement for the speed of light.

Jean Foucault (1819–1868), Fizeau's former assistant, improved on Fizeau's apparatus and measurements.

Albert Michelson (1852–1931), a U.S. physicist and Nobel Prize win-ner, obtained what is considered to be the first really accurate mea-surement for the speed of light.

LIGHT TIME

Light travels very fast. So fast, in fact, that to us it appears to travel instantly from one place to another. However, light does have a finite speed. Light travels at 299,792,458 meters (about 186,282 miles) per second in a vacuum. Light is slower when passing through transparent materials, such as air, water, or glass. Even so, it is difficult to imagine this kind of speed. To get an idea of how fast light travels, compare the time it takes for light to travel from different objects to the boy pictured in bed.

Because light is so fast, the distance it travels over a period of 1 year is sometimes used as a measure of astronomical distances. This unit of measure is called a light-year. The light-year unit is sometimes used by astronomers to measure the vast distances between stars and even between galaxies. A light-year is therefore a measure of distance, not time! One light-year is equal to about 9,500,000,000,000 kilometers (9.5×10^{12} km). ☐

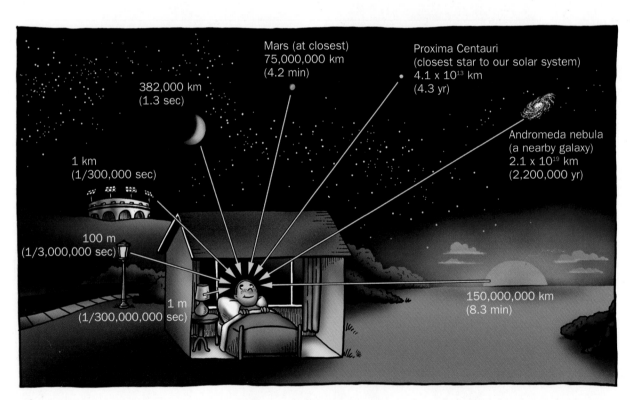

When you look at the Moon, you are actually seeing it as it was 1.3 seconds ago. If you glance up at the Sun, you are seeing it as it was about 8.3 minutes ago. That's how long it took the light the boy sees to travel to the boy's eyes. If you used a telescope to view distant galaxies, you would see them as they were millions of years ago! The finite speed of light allows astronomers to see into the past and unravel the history of our universe.

Compared with other galaxies, the Andromeda galaxy is close to Earth. Light from the Andromeda galaxy takes 2.2 million years to reach Earth. Estimates are that light from the most distant objects in the universe takes over 13 billion years to reach Earth.

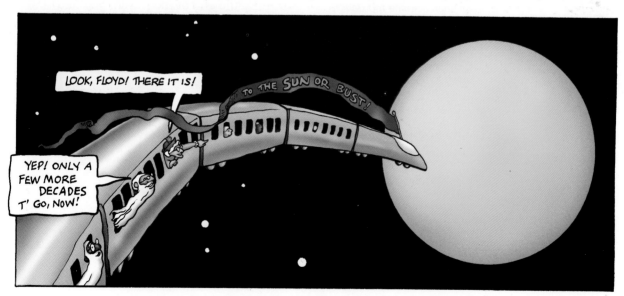

A high-speed train, traveling at about 240 kilometers (150 miles) per hour, would take about 75 years—an entire lifetime—to travel to the Sun. Yet, it takes light only 8.3 minutes to cover the same distance.

How Light Spreads Out

UNITED STATES DEPARTMENT OF THE INTERIOR/NATIONAL PARK SERVICE/WIND CAVE NATIONAL PARK

If you moved far from a fire such as this one, it would soon become too dark to see your surroundings. Do you know why?

INTRODUCTION

What happens to light when it leaves a light source? You got some clues in Lesson 3 when you observed light from a flashlight travel through cloudy water. Think about some other light sources. The Sun, our nearest star, is a huge ball of glowing gas. Where does all the Sun's light go? Does all of it reach Earth? There are millions of other stars in our galaxy—billions in our universe—and many of these stars are much bigger than the Sun. So why isn't the night sky bright with the light these stars produce? Why do these giant stars appear so small and dim when observed from Earth? What about other light sources? For example, what appears to happen to car headlights when they move toward or away from you? Does their brightness appear to change? In this lesson, you will investigate how light behaves after it leaves a light source. By the end of the lesson, you may find it easier to answer some of these questions.

OBJECTIVES FOR THIS LESSON

Investigate whether the appearance of a light source depends on your distance from it.

Investigate the way light behaves as it travels from a light source.

Getting Started

1. One member of your group should collect the plastic box of materials. Remove the flashlight from the box.

2. Working with your partner, shine the flashlight on the wall. What do you see on the wall? Move the flashlight backward and forward. Describe in your science notebook what you observe on the wall.

3. Discuss your observations with your partner. How can you explain your observations? Record your ideas (as sentences or diagrams) in your notebook.

4. Stand at one end of the room. Your partner should be about 2 meters (m) in front of you and should shine the flashlight in your face. Have him or her walk to the other end of the room while pointing the flashlight at you. Observe any changes in the appearance of the flashlight as your partner moves away from you. Record your observations in your notebook. Does the flashlight change in appearance? If so, can you explain why? Record your ideas.

MATERIALS FOR LESSON 4

For you
1 copy of Student Sheet 4.1: Measuring Light and Distance

For you and your lab partner
1 flashlight
2 D-cell batteries
1 assembled light stand
4 binder clips
1 sheet of paper with 1-cm × 1-cm squares
1 white screen
1 black card with a 1-cm × 1-cm hole
1 meterstick
2 plastic stands
1 box of colored pencils

Inquiry 4.1
Measuring Light and Distance

PROCEDURE

1. In this inquiry, you will investigate in more detail the way light behaves when it leaves a light source. You will be recording your observations, results, and explanations on Student Sheet 4.1: Measuring Light and Distance.

2. Divide the remaining materials between the pairs in your group. Put the meterstick on a desk.

3. Attach two binder clips to the short sides of the card with the hole so it stands up (see Figure 4.1). Position the card with the hole exactly 10 centimeters (cm) from the beginning of the meterstick. Place the light stand in a horizontal position, so the end of the lightbulb filament is at the beginning of the meterstick.

Figure 4.1 *Use two binder clips to make the card with the hole stand up. Position the card so the hole is 10 cm from the beginning of the meterstick and the tip of the filament of the lightbulb.*

4. Use the other binder clips to attach the paper with 1-cm squares to the screen. Attach the plastic stands to the sides of the screen (see Figure 4.2). (You may need to gently pry the plastic stands open with your fingers.)

5. Stand the screen and the card next to each other so that they are touching. (You will need to bend the card a little so that it touches the screen.) Keep the light source horizontal at the beginning of the meterstick. Make sure the end of the filament is aligned with the hole in the card. The light will shine through the hole in the card (see Figure 4.3).

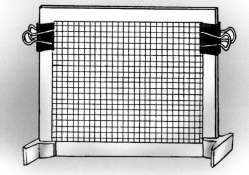

Figure 4.2 *Use the other binder clips to attach the squared paper to the screen. Attach the plastic stands to the sides of the screen.*

Figure 4.3 *Make sure the end of the filament is aligned with the hole in the card. Position the screen and the card next to each other so that they touch.*

6. What area of the squared paper does the light illuminate? Use a colored pencil to record the approximate area illuminated by tracing its outline on the squared paper on the screen. This is the area illuminated through the hole when the screen is 10 cm from the light source. Use the same colored pencil to record the distance of the screen from the light source (the beginning of the meterstick) inside the area you outlined on the squared paper.

Figure 4.4 *Use a colored pencil to trace the outline of the illuminated area on the squared paper.*

7. Do not move the lightbulb or the card with the hole. Move the screen 10 cm away from the card with the hole. Use a colored pencil of a different color to trace the area illuminated on the squared paper in the same way (see Figure 4.4). How far is the screen from the light source? Record this distance inside the area you outlined on the squared paper.

8. Repeat the procedure with the screen 30 cm, 40 cm, and 50 cm from the light source. For each distance, determine the approximate area of the squared paper illuminated through the hole.

A. Design a table for your results. Complete the table.

B. Plot a graph of your results. You will need to decide on the axes you are going to use and the type of graph you should plot.

C. Is there any mathematical relationship between the distance of the screen from the light source and the area of illumination on the screen? If there is, describe it.

D. Use your data and graph to predict the area that would be illuminated if the screen was placed 60 cm and 80 cm from the light source. Record your predictions.

REFLECTING ON WHAT YOU'VE DONE

1. How do you think light spreads out from a lightbulb? Record your responses on the student sheet. Be prepared to share your responses with the class.

A. Draw a diagram that shows how light spreads out from the lightbulb onto the screen.

B. Write a paragraph explaining why a light source appears less bright as you move away from it. Think about the following questions before you write your explanation:

Does the brightness of the light source really change?

What happens to light when it leaves the source?

Does the light always shine on the same size area?

2. Some stars (apart from our Sun) look very small—sometimes just pinpoints of light—and dim.

C. Why is this so? Write a sentence giving your ideas.

3. Review the question bank cards generated in Lesson 1. Can you answer any more of them now? Identify those you feel comfortable answering.

LIGHT and DISTANCE

Why do lights look dimmer when they are farther away? In Inquiry 4.1, you determined that light spreads out from its source. Think about what happens when you quickly turn a lightbulb on and off again? A flash or pulse of light is produced. This pulse of light can be thought of as moving away from the lightbulb in all directions, like a shell or hollow sphere of light. The farther the pulse of light is from the lightbulb, the bigger the hollow sphere of light becomes.

As the sphere of light gets bigger, the light spreads out. The area illuminated by the pulse of light increases very quickly. The *amount* of light reaching each square centimeter gets smaller. This explains why the farther you get from a light source, the less bright it appears.

The apparent brightness of light, or how it looks to your eyes, decreases much more quickly than you might think. This is because

> Hey, it looks as though something's coming. I can just make out its lights.

> Wow! Those headlights are bright!

> There goes my night vision!

When this lightbulb flashes, light spreads out from it in all directions like a shell or hollow sphere of light.

I can barely see its tail lights now.

Yeah, they're much dimmer

Why do distant lights look dim, and yet when they get close, they're really bright?

Ah, that's physics–*my favorite* subject!

the area over which the light spreads—the surface area of the hollow sphere of light—grows faster than the distance the light travels. In your inquiry, when you doubled the distance from the lightbulb (from 10 to 20 cm) the light spread out over an area four times as large.

Observed from this distance, the lightbulb appears one-fourth as bright. Double the distance again, this time to 40 cm, and the same lightbulb appears only one-sixteenth as bright!

This rapid change in the apparent brightness of light as you move away from its source is sometimes called the inverse square law, which is shown in the following equation:

Apparent brightness = Brightness at source/distance^2

This law explains why bright street lamps can be seen for only a few miles and why it gets dark quickly when you walk away from a nighttime campfire. ☐

Doing the Math on Spreading Light

The following equations give some mathematical proof for inverse square law:
The area illuminated by a sphere of light is—
$4 \times \pi \times$ radius of the sphere^2

If the approximate value of π is taken as 3.14, then:
The area illuminated by a sphere of light with a radius of 10 cm is
$4 \times 3.14 \times 10 \times 10 = 1256$ cm^2

The area illuminated by a sphere of light with a radius of 20 cm is
$4 \times 3.14 \times 20 \times 20 = 5024$ cm^2

What will be the area illuminated by a sphere of light if the sphere of light has a radius of 30 cm?

Blocking the Light

Your shadow follows you everywhere. How is it formed? Is it always the same size or shape? Do you always have only one shadow?

© ROB CASEY/PHOTODISC/PICTUREQUEST

INTRODUCTION

Light can pass through the vacuum of space. You know this because light from the Sun reaches Earth. You have observed during your experiments that light can travel through air and through water, some types of plastic, and glass. But can light travel through all types of matter? Does it pass through different types of matter in the same way? In this lesson, you will try to answer these questions.

OBJECTIVES FOR THIS LESSON

Observe what happens when light strikes different materials.

Investigate and explain the appearance and formation of shadows.

Getting Started

1. Have one member of your group collect the bag of objects.

2. Spread the contents of the bag out on a desk.

3. Examine the objects. Work with your group to sort the objects into groupings according to how they allow light to pass through them.

4. Create a table in your science notebook to list your groupings and record the objects in each grouping.

For you
- 1 copy of Student Sheet 5.1: Putting Objects in the Path of Light
- 1 copy of Student Sheet 5.2: Measuring Shadow Size

For you and your lab partner
- 1 assembled light stand
- 1 meterstick
- 1 white screen
- 2 plastic stands
- 1 black disk
- 1 craft stick
- Masking tape

For your group
- 1 bag containing samples of paper, plastic, cardboard, and other objects

Inquiry 5.1
Putting Objects in the Path of Light

PROCEDURE

1. Have one member of your group collect the plastic box of materials. Divide the materials between the pairs in your group.

2. Record your observations, measurements, and explanations on Student Sheet 5.1: Putting Objects in the Path of Light.

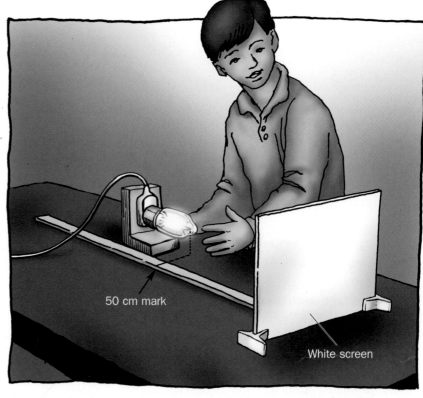

Figure 5.1 *Set up the screen. Place the lightbulb in a horizontal position. Put your hand between the screen and the lightbulb.*

3. Working with your partner, set up the screen. Place the light stand so the lightbulb is horizontal. Position the lightbulb so the tip of its filament is 50 cm away from the screen. Put your hand between the lightbulb and the screen (see Figure 5.1).

SAFETY TIP

Lightbulbs become hot very quickly and take many minutes to cool down. Make sure your lightbulb is cool before you handle it.

4. Switch on the lightbulb.

A. What do you observe on the screen? Use words and/or a diagram to explain what you see.

5. Hold each object from "Getting Started" about 20 cm from the screen.

B. For each object, describe what you see on the screen. Create a table to record your descriptions.

6. Discuss your observations with your partner.

C. Explain what you observe.

D. What do you think causes a shadow to form?

E. Which of your objects produces the darkest shadows?

TRANSPARENT, TRANSLUCENT, AND OPAQUE

Substances that let light of certain wavelengths pass through them and can be clearly seen through are called transparent. Water, glass, and acetate sheets are transparent. Colored glass is also transparent—it allows some colors through but not others. Materials that let light pass through but cannot be clearly seen through are called translucent. These materials are said to diffuse, or scatter, light. Wax paper and frosted glass are two examples of translucent substances. Materials that do not let light pass through them are called opaque. Sometimes, thin samples of opaque materials (thin paper, for example) may be translucent in bright light.

All matter interacts in some way with light. Water, for example, is fairly transparent, but it does absorb and scatter some light. As a diver goes deeper into the sea, the color of the light from the Sun changes—it gets bluer and darker. Sunlight cannot penetrate the deepest part of the oceans.

Water is considered transparent, but it does absorb and scatter some light. This is one reason why light does not reach the deepest part of the oceans. Submariners must carry their light with them.

Clouds may allow light to pass through them, but you cannot see through them. They are translucent.

Inquiry 5.2
Measuring Shadow Size

PROCEDURE

1. You will be working with your partner. Record all your observations, measurements, and explanations on Student Sheet 5.2: Measuring Shadow Size.

2. Switch on the lightbulb.

   A. Put your hand between the screen and the lightbulb and move your hand backward and forward between the lightbulb and the screen. Describe what you observe.

3. Attach the black disk to the craft stick (see Figure 5.2).

   B. Measure and record the diameter of the disk.

Figure 5.2 *Use tape to attach the disk to the craft stick.*

4. Use the disk to make a shadow on the screen. Hold the disk 20 cm from the screen.

   C. Draw the shadow produced by the disk.

5. You are going to measure the size of the shadow made by the disk when it is placed at different distances from the screen. Start by measuring the diameter of the shadow produced when the disk is 20 cm from the screen. You should make at least five measurements of shadow diameter with the disk at different distances from the screen.

   D. Design and draw a table for your results.

6. Place the disk at different distances from the screen that you have chosen to record and measure the diameter of the shadow produced each time (see Figure 5.3). Record your results in the table.

Figure 5.3 *Place the disk at different distances from the screen. Measure the diameter of the shadow the disk produces.*

E. Present your results as a graph.

F. Is there a relationship between the diameter of the shadow produced by the disk and the distance of the disk from the screen? Record your ideas.

G. Use a diagram to explain what you observed. Be prepared to draw your diagram for the class to discuss.

Inquiry 5.3
Comparing Shadows

PROCEDURE

1. Place the lightbulb in a vertical position, as shown in Figure 5.4. Use the disk to make a shadow on the screen. Record your responses for this inquiry in your notebook.

A. Draw a diagram of the shadow produced.

B. Describe how the shadow formed when the lightbulb was placed vertically differs from the shadow formed when the lightbulb was placed horizontally.

C. Have you ever seen a shadow like this before? If so, where?

2. After a class discussion about shadows, add labels to your diagram from A.

D. Draw a diagram that explains how fuzzy shadows are produced.

Figure 5.4 *Move the light stand so that the lightbulb is in a vertical position. Use the disk to make a shadow.*

ASTRONOMICAL SHADOWS

Shadows are areas of darkness that form behind an object when the object blocks a source of light. When shadows are formed on an astronomical scale, they are given a special name. They are called eclipses.

From Earth, two types of eclipses are visible to the naked eye—lunar eclipses and solar eclipses. A lunar eclipse occurs when Earth comes between the Sun and Moon and casts a shadow on the Moon. A solar eclipse happens when the Moon casts its shadow on Earth.

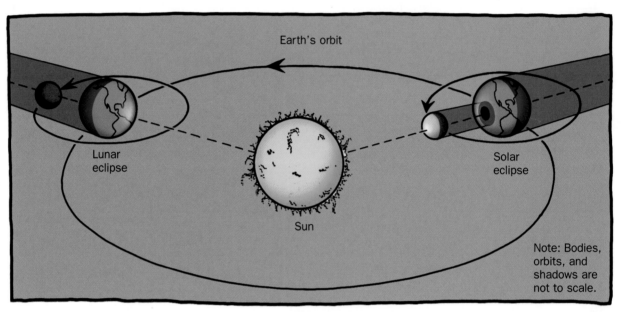

Note: Bodies, orbits, and shadows are not to scale.

The shadows made by an eclipse have two regions, the umbra and penumbra. You may have observed these regions of a shadow in Inquiry 5.3. During a solar eclipse, the area under the umbra is in almost complete darkness. The area under the penumbra becomes about as dark as a dark, cloudy day.

A lunar eclipse in progress: a series of pictures taken at different times during an eclipse. You can see the shadow of Earth moving across the Moon's surface. Why in a total eclipse does the Moon look red? A later lesson will help you answer this question.

REFLECTING ON WHAT YOU'VE DONE

1. After discussing A–D with your group, record your responses in your notebook:

A. How are shadows produced?

B. What is the relationship between the size of a shadow on the screen and the distance of the screen from the object that produces the shadow?

C. What is the relationship between the size of a shadow on the screen and the distance of the object from the light source?

D. Which types of light sources produce the sharpest shadows?

2. Is it possible for an object to cast more than one shadow? You will need to share materials with other pairs and groups to help you answer this question.

E. Write a short paragraph about what you discovered.

3. Review the question bank cards generated in Lesson 1. Can you answer any more of them now? Identify those that you feel comfortable answering.

Theater of Shadows

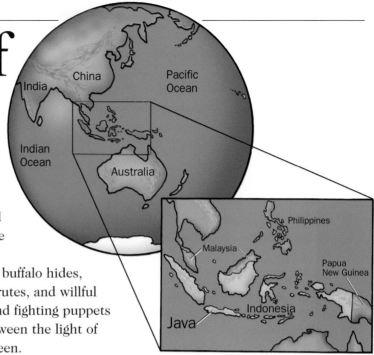

It began nearly one thousand years ago on the island nation of Indonesia. Shadow masters, called dalangs, traveled from village to village entertaining people with tales of love and war.

They used flat puppets, made of water buffalo hides, to play the parts of brave princes, evil brutes, and willful heroines. The shadows of the dancing and fighting puppets were created by placing the puppets between the light of an oil-burning lamp and a thin cloth screen.

The villagers looked forward to the dalang's visits. They gathered at the village square or temple yard at sunset to watch and listen. And that's just what they did—until dawn of the next day! To the people of Indonesia, the long plays were well worth it. The stories were morality tales that reminded the adults, and taught the children, about the nature of good and evil. And they believed that the puppets' shadows were their ancestors' spirits returning to Earth.

Shadow puppet theater is a traditional form of entertainment in much of the archipelago that makes up Indonesia. Tamara first watched puppet masters at work on her home island of Java.

As a child in Indonesia, Tamara was fascinated by shadow puppet theater. Now she shares her enjoyment and knowledge of it with a new generation of youngsters.

The Magic and the Stories

Tamara Fielding was born in Indonesia on the island of Java. As a child, she was not supposed to go behind the dalang's screen to watch him perform. Only men and boys were allowed to do that. But young Tamara couldn't resist. She secretly crept behind the screen and watched the dalang work. His skillful and graceful performance amazed her. So did the beauty and fierceness of the puppets. From that early exposure, the "magic and the stories of shadow theater were locked inside me," says Tamara. And there they would stay for many years.

Tamara moved to Europe in her 20s. She studied drama and theater in Paris. Eventually, she came to the United States, where she continued her acting career. More years went by. Then one day, Tamara decided to dust off the shadow puppets that relatives had given her years before. She built a cloth screen and started moving the puppets in a way she remembered the dalang doing so long ago. The magic and the stories inside her began to come out.

Shadow Figures

Now Tamara has more than 400 puppets, or "shadow figures," as she calls them. She travels—not from village to village—but to universities, museums, and festivals sharing the stories and art of shadow theater.

Wearing a sarong and lace blouse with a flower in her hair, Tamara sits on the floor between the screen and the light. Unlike dalangs of old, she uses a 600-Watt halogen lamp to create her shadows. And most of her performances last less than an hour—not all night.

Today the shadow figures are as lively and powerful as ever. Like dalangs of old, Tamara creates the many voices of her characters. Her varied cast includes heroes, princesses, and animals, including monkeys, tigers, elephants, birds, and snakes.

With a single light source and a piece of cloth, the many dark shapes come alive. In the magical world of shadow theater, the shadows—magnificent, beautiful, and loathsome—take center stage. ☐

This traditional Indonesian play is about ancestors' spirits returning to Earth at night. The colors of these puppets are not visible. The audience sees only the puppets' shadows.

6

The Pinhole Camera

This girl is viewing the world through a pinhole. How is her view different than what she would see using just her naked eye?

INTRODUCTION

You have collected evidence to support the hypothesis that light travels in straight lines. You have used this hypothesis to explain (using ray diagrams) how light spreads out from a source and how shadows are formed. In this lesson, you will construct a device called a pinhole camera. Your pinhole camera does not take photographs, but it will provide you with a surprising picture of the world. How is this picture produced? Can you explain the picture's appearance using a ray diagram? Does changing the design of the pinhole camera alter the picture it produces?

OBJECTIVES FOR THIS LESSON

Build a pinhole camera.

Observe how a pinhole camera works.

Use ray diagrams to explain how a pinhole camera works.

Getting Started

1. Have one member of your group collect the plastic box of materials. Divide the materials between the pairs in your group.

2. Wrap a piece of aluminum foil over one end of the narrow tube, folding it down the side of the tube (see Figure 6.1).

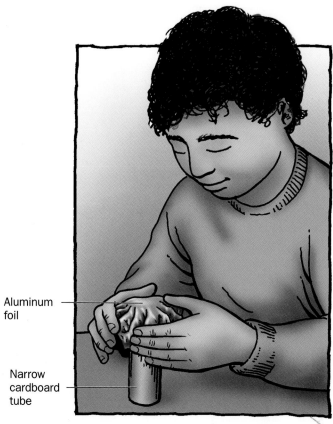

Aluminum foil

Narrow cardboard tube

Figure 6.1 *Wrap the aluminum foil over the end of the narrow tube.*

MATERIALS FOR LESSON 6

For you
- 1 copy of Student Sheet 6.1: Looking Through Your Pinhole Camera
- 1 copy of Student Sheet 6.2: Modifying Your Pinhole Camera

For you and your lab partner
- 1 narrow cardboard tube
- 1 wide cardboard tube
- 2 pieces of aluminum foil
- 1 square of white plastic sheet
- 1 paper clip
- 2 rubber bands
- 1 piece of black paper
  Masking tape

For your group
- 1 transparency (or sheet of newsprint)
- 2 transparency markers or regular markers

3. Secure the foil in place by wrapping a rubber band around the foil and the tube as shown in Figure 6.2. Make sure the foil is smooth and flat. Take care—it tears easily!

4. Straighten the paper clip. Being very careful not to tear the foil, use the paperclip to make a single tiny hole in the center of the foil (see Figure 6.3).

5. Wrap the piece of white plastic sheet over one end of the wide tube. Make sure the sheet is as flat as possible. Use a rubber band to secure the sheet in place (see Figure 6.4).

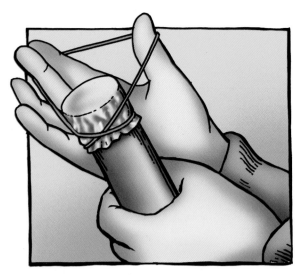

Figure 6.2 *Secure the foil by wrapping a rubber band around the foil and the tube.*

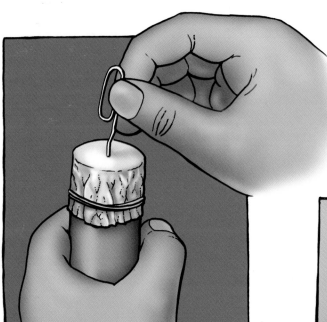

Figure 6.3 *Use a straightened paper clip to make a tiny hole in the center of the foil.*

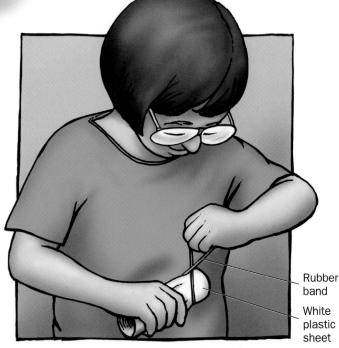

Rubber band

White plastic sheet

Figure 6.4 *Make sure the white plastic sheet is flat before securing it with a rubber band.*

6. Slide the open end of the narrow tube inside the open end of the wide tube. Push the narrow tube about three-fourths of the way into the wide tube.

7. Roll the black paper so that it fits over the wide tube as shown in Figure 6.5. Use tape to attach the black paper to the white plastic end of the tube. Your pinhole camera is ready to use!

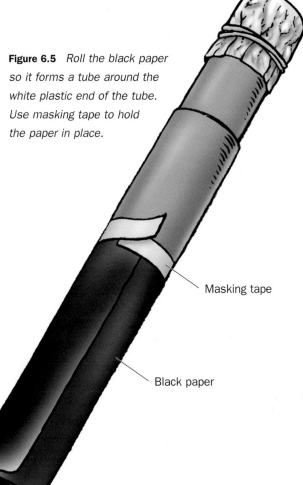

Figure 6.5 *Roll the black paper so it forms a tube around the white plastic end of the tube. Use masking tape to hold the paper in place.*

Masking tape

Black paper

Inquiry 6.1
Looking Through Your Pinhole Camera

PROCEDURE

1. Record your predictions, observations, explanations, and diagrams for this inquiry on Student Sheet 6.1: Looking Through Your Pinhole Camera.

2. Your teacher has set out some lamps and other objects to look at through your pinhole camera. Choose an item to look at using your pinhole camera. Point the foil end of the camera at the object. Look through the white plastic end (see Figure 6.6).

A. What do you observe on the white plastic?

B. Compare what you observe through the pinhole camera with what you observe using only your eyes. What is the difference between the two views?

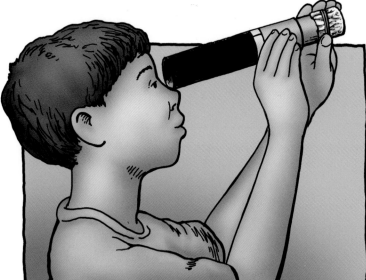

Figure 6.6 *Look through the white plastic end of your pinhole camera. The black paper will shade the white plastic from unwanted light.*

3. Look at other objects through the pinhole camera.

C. Which objects are easy to see on the white plastic?

D. Which objects are not easy to see?

E. Think about how light gets into the pinhole camera. Why do you think some objects are easier to see than others?

4. The picture on the white plastic of the pinhole camera is called an image. The white plastic acts as a screen on which the image forms. Discuss with your partner where else you may have seen an image formed on a screen.

5. Look at the diagram of the pinhole camera in Figure 6.7. The same diagram is on Student Sheet 6.1.

F. On the diagram on the student sheet, draw a line from the top of the object (Point A) that represents light leaving the object, passing through the pinhole, and forming an image on the screen. Next draw a line from Point B that represents light leaving the object, passing through the pinhole, and forming an image on the screen.

6. How does your diagram help you understand what is happening to light inside the pinhole camera? Discuss the following questions with your partner before answering them on the student sheet:

G. What happens to the rays of light from the object as they pass through the tiny hole?

H. How does your diagram help you explain the appearance of the image on the screen?

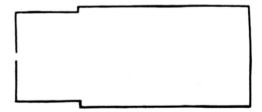

Figure 6.7 *Complete this diagram on the student sheet.*

Inquiry 6.2
Modifying Your Pinhole Camera

PROCEDURE

1. Working with your partner, you will now make changes in your camera and predict, observe, and explain how these changes affect how light behaves when it passes into your camera. Record your predictions, observations, explanations, and diagrams for this inquiry on Student Sheet 6.2: Modifying Your Pinhole Camera.

2. Predict what will happen to the image on the screen if you extend the length of the pinhole camera.

   A. Record your prediction.

3. Pull the narrow tube part of the way out of the wide tube so the camera is longer.

   B. Describe your observations.

   C. Draw a diagram that explains your observations.

4. Predict what will happen to the image on the screen if you double the diameter of the hole in the foil.

D. Record your prediction. Test it, and record your observations and any explanations you have.

5. Predict what will happen to the image on the screen if you make more than one hole in the foil.

E. Record your prediction. Test it, and record your observations. Be prepared to share your results with the class.

6. Discuss with other students in your group what you think is happening to light to produce the effect you observed in Step 5. On the transparency (or newsprint), draw a diagram that explains how light behaves when it passes into a pinhole camera with two holes. Be prepared to present your ideas and diagram to the class.

REFLECTING ON WHAT YOU'VE DONE

Discuss with other students in your group what a pinhole camera is and how it works. Listen to their explanations. Ask each other questions to determine whether you all understand what you have observed during the lesson.

A. Write a paragraph under A on Student Sheet 6.2, in your own words, that describes what a pinhole camera is and explains how it works. Be prepared to share your paragraph with the class.

This picture was taken using a pinhole camera. Although pictures taken with a pinhole camera often have a "soft" appearance, they have a very large depth of field. Notice how objects in the front of the picture and in the back of the picture are all equally in focus.

Pictures Through a Pinhole

COURTESY OF GEORGE EASTMAN HOUSE

What use is a camera without film? Not much, you might say. But the first cameras had no film. In fact, some of the earliest cameras were dark rooms with a small hole in one wall. (The word "camera" actually means "room.") These rooms were giant pinhole cameras. This type of pinhole camera was called a camera obscura.

A person sat inside the room and secretly observed an upside-down image of the outside world projected onto the wall opposite the hole. Artists often used a camera obscura to trace an outline of a landscape onto paper or canvas. Some artists had portable camera obscuras—and lots of servants to carry them about! Other artists made smaller versions. Still others added lenses to the cameras to focus the light in order to make a bigger and brighter picture.

Pinhole Cameras and Photography

The invention of photography in the early 19th century meant that a camera could reproduce an image and make a picture automatically. However, the design of a modern camera remains similar to that of a pinhole camera. New parts have been added, but a modern camera still basically consists of a box with a hole in it.

Some photographers still use pinhole cameras (with photographic film, but no lenses) to take photographs. Pictures taken with pinhole cameras often have a "soft" appearance, that is, the images are not sharply defined. However, they have a very large depth of field. This means that objects in the front of the picture and in the back of the picture are all equally in focus.

Because only a small amount of light enters the pinhole, a pinhole camera requires very bright light or a long exposure time. (Exposure time is the length of time the light is allowed to fall on the film.) Modern cameras use a larger hole (or aperture) and lenses to collect and focus more light. This allows pictures to be taken under dimmer conditions. Modern cameras also use short exposure times—usually hundredths of a second. This allows the camera to take clear photos of moving objects. But the larger aperture possible with modern cameras has some drawbacks. Look at the photo of chickens taken with a modern camera. Are the near and far objects equally in focus?

When using a large aperture and a lens, a camera has a much smaller depth of field than a pinhole camera. This results in a photograph in which only some of the objects are in focus.

Pinhole Cameras and Science

Pinhole cameras are useful scientific instruments. In the 4th century B.C., the philosopher Aristotle used a pinhole in a leaf to observe eclipses of the Sun. We still use pinholes to look at an image of the Sun without damaging our eyes. (Find out more about this method before trying it out!)

This painting is by the aptly named artist, Canaletto. He used a camera obscura to make exact drawings from which he produced many detailed paintings, some showing the famous canals of his hometown of Venice, Italy.

Some satellites designed to look at distant stars are equipped with versions of the pinhole camera. Scientists and engineers often use pinhole cameras to observe and take photographs of very bright images. Rocket designers use them to photograph the behavior of brightly burning hot gases inside rocket engines. Physicists studying the process by which the Sun releases energy use them to photograph gases heated up (by lasers) to temperatures similar to the surface of the Sun.

The pinhole camera may be an old invention, but it still has a lot of new uses. □

Camera obscuras were small rooms or very large boxes, some big enough to stand inside. This giant camera was used by an artist in the 17th century. It was supposed to be portable—if you had the servants to carry it around.

When using a modern camera with a lens and a large aperture only some of the objects can be brought into focus. In this photograph, only some of the chickens are in focus.

7

Modeling Light

What happens to some of the movement energy of this boy when he hits the water? What is produced, and what does this have to do with light?

INTRODUCTION

You have spent the last few lessons investigating some of the characteristics of light. You looked at how light is produced and how it spreads out from a light source. You determined that light travels in straight lines and can travel through air and the vacuum of space. You compared the behavior of light when it strikes transparent, opaque, and translucent objects. You used what you have discovered to explain the formation of shadows and images in a pinhole camera using simple ray diagrams. You already know quite a lot about how light behaves!

But what gives light these characteristics? How are the characteristics of light related to one another? What is the exact nature of light? Is there some way you can better understand what light is? Can you use your knowledge of the nature of light to explain why it behaves in particular ways? Can you predict how it will behave in different situations?

One way you can better understand what light is and why it behaves as it does is by using scientific models. After you revisit your ideas about the nature of light, you will discuss the nature of scientific models and then use two scientific models for light. At the end of this lesson, you will be asked to compare how well these models explain what you observed in previous lessons.

OBJECTIVES FOR THIS LESSON

Discuss the nature of light.

Use and compare scientific models for light.

Getting Started

1. In Lesson 1, you were asked the question, What is light? Think about the question again. Discuss any new ideas you have with your group. Have your ideas about the nature of light changed? Have other members of your group reached similar conclusions? In your science notebook, write what you now think light is.

2. If light is a form of energy, how does it move from one place to another? Look at Figure 7.1. What is happening in each photograph? These pictures may give you some ideas about how energy can be moved from one place to another.

3. Discuss your ideas with the class.

4. Read "Scientific Models."

MATERIALS FOR LESSON 7

For you

1	copy of Student Sheet 7.1: Using Particles To Model Light
1	copy of Student Sheet 7.2: Using Waves To Model Light

For your group

15	ball bearings (in a resealable plastic bag)
1	straight metal barrier
1	transparent tray
1	cardboard tube
1	transparent cup
1	wooden dowel
1	folding lamp
4	AA batteries
2	wooden blocks
1	dropping bottle
1	metric ruler, 30 cm (12″)
1	cork
1	sheet of white paper

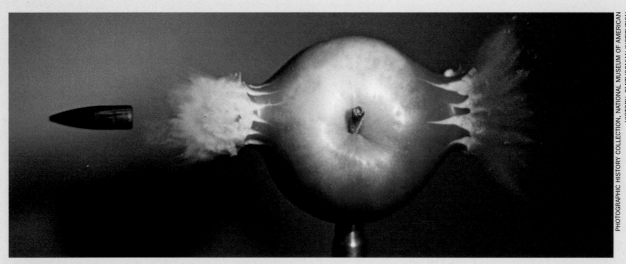

PHOTOGRAPHIC HISTORY COLLECTION, NATIONAL MUSEUM OF AMERICAN HISTORY, SMITHSONIAN INSTITUTION

How was energy from a gun transferred to this target?

NATIONAL GEOPHYSICAL DATA CENTER

How was energy from a distant earthquake transferred to these buildings?

CORBIS/ROYALTY-FREE

CORBIS/ROYALTY-FREE

What makes this surfer move? Where did the energy come from? How did it get to the surfer?

Whoever kicked this ball is about to transfer the energy to the boy's head. How did this energy transfer take place?

Figure 7.1 *How is energy being moved from one place to another?*

SCIENTIFIC MODELS

In this lesson, you will investigate two scientific models for light. A scientific model is a way of thinking about how something works. It is not a copy of an object like a plastic model of an airplane or the human body. Scientific models help scientists understand complex processes or systems that are difficult to understand or observe.

You may already have used scientific models. For example, have you ever used a model of the structure of the atom? You might have also used a model to explain how electrical energy moves around a circuit.

Before scientists construct a scientific model, they closely observe what they are studying. Next, they try to link these observations. Then they design a model that behaves in the same way. The model may be a mathematical one. Today's scientists often simulate models on computers. Or they may make models from materials that *behave like* the thing they are modeling.

Scientists may use scientific models to help predict how the things they are studying will behave. A good model can be used to make accurate predictions. For example, weather forecasters use computer models of Earth's weather (based on lots of data collected from around the world).

Scientists commonly use two scientific models for light: the particle (or photon) model and the wave model. Both can be partly represented using materials that are easy to observe and that sometimes behave in ways similar to light. You will use both models in this lesson.

Accurate models behave just like the things they are modeling. But most scientific models have limitations. They can demonstrate and help explain only some of the observations made by scientists. You will compare the particle and wave models with your own observations and knowledge about light. Is one model better? Think about and evaluate these two models as you work through this module. You will revisit both later in the module.

Inquiry 7.1
Using Particles To Model Light

PROCEDURE

1. One member of your group should collect the plastic box of materials. You will record your observations and explanations for this inquiry on Student Sheet 7.1: Using Particles To Model Light.

2. In this inquiry, you will use small ball bearings to model the behavior of light. Take the plastic bag of ball bearings out of the box. Look at and handle them. Discuss with your group how you could use a ball bearing to transfer energy from one place to another.

3. Roll a few ball bearings down the tube and across the flat surface of the transparent tray (see Figure 7.2).

   A. Record any energy transformations taking place as the ball bearings move from the top of the tube until after they strike the end of the tray.

Figure 7.2 *Roll a few ball bearings down the tube and across the transparent tray.*

B. How do the ball bearings behave as they travel across the flat surface? Describe how this aspect of the ball bearing model compares with what you know about light.

4. In Lesson 4, you investigated how light spreads out from a source. Try modeling this using the ball bearings. Hold the tube vertically with one end about 1 cm above the surface of the tray. Use a small piece of scrap paper to help you drop all the ball bearings into the tube at once (as shown in Figure 7.3).

C. How do the ball bearings behave? How does their behavior compare with the way light behaves when it spreads out from a source?

5. Think about the shadows you investigated in Lesson 5. If the ball bearings represent light, how can you use the ball bearings, metal barrier, and tray to model shadows? Design and set up a model shadow in the tray.

D. Draw your model design.

E. Describe (using words and a diagram) what happened when you tested your model.

F. Compare what happened in your model to how light behaves.

6. Discuss the following questions with your group:

Figure 7.3 *Holding the end of the tube about 1 cm above the tray, drop all the ball bearings into the tube at once.*

Is the ball bearing model (usually called a particle model) for light a useful model?

What are its limitations? (How does it fall short in explaining what you already know about light?)

How could the model be improved?

7. Return the ball bearings to the resealable bag. Be sure to seal the top of the bag.

Inquiry 7.2
Using Waves To Model Light

PROCEDURE

1. Record your observations and explanations for this inquiry on Student Sheet 7.2: Using Waves To Model Light. Your teacher will show you how to set up and use a ripple tank.

2. Set up your ripple tank, using Figures 7.4–7.6 as a guide.

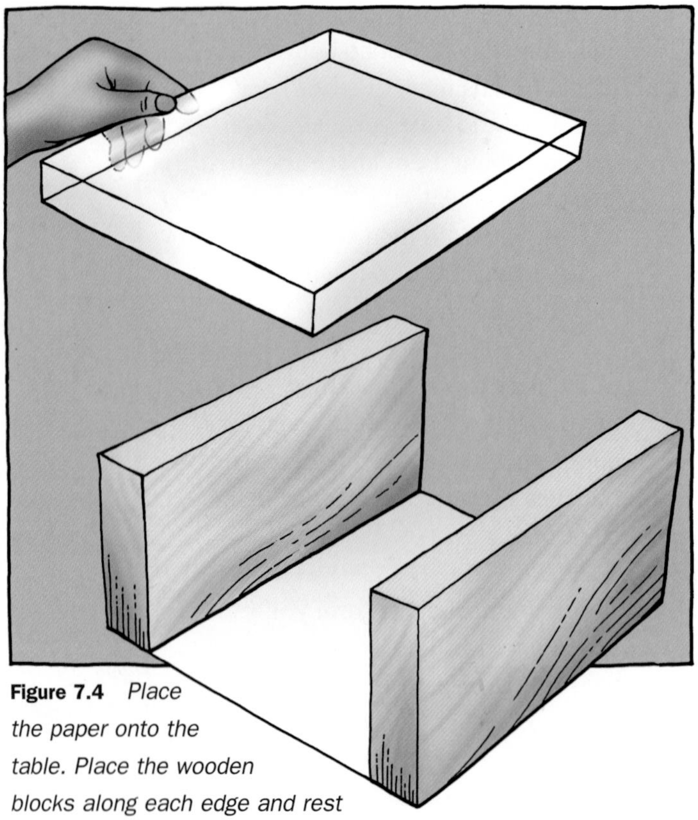

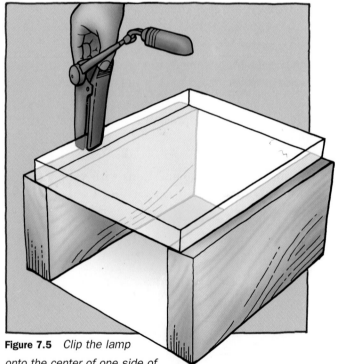

Figure 7.4 *Place the paper onto the table. Place the wooden blocks along each edge and rest the tray across the top of the blocks.*

SAFETY TIP

Make sure the battery box of the lamp is out-side of the tray and does not touch the water.

Figure 7.5 *Clip the lamp onto the center of one side of the tray. Make sure that the battery box is on the outside of the tray and the lightbulb is positioned over the center of the tray.*

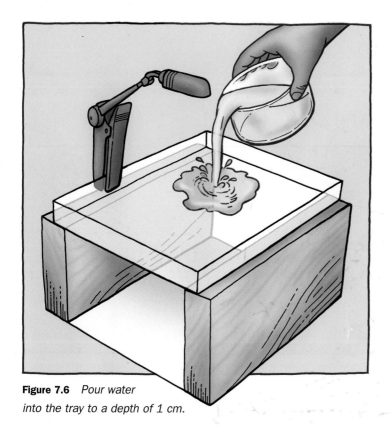

Figure 7.6 *Pour water into the tray to a depth of 1 cm.*

3. Float the cork in the water at one end of the tray. How can you transfer energy from your finger at one corner of the tray to the cork at the other end of the tray without touching the cork? Try out your ideas.

A. Describe what you did and what you observed.

B. Identify any energy transformations that took place.

4. Remove the cork from the tray. Switch on the lamp.

5. Use the dropping bottle to drop one drop of water into the center of the tray. Look carefully at the paper.

C. Draw and describe what you observe.

D. How does the behavior of the water around the drop compare with the behavior of light as it spreads out from a light source?

6. Your teacher will demonstrate how to generate waves using the wooden dowel. Practice generating waves (see Figure 7.7) by making—

- a single wave that travels the length of the tray.
- the waves as straight as possible.
- five or six closely spaced waves travel the length of the tray at one time.

7. Observe the waves on the sheet of paper below the tray.

E. What do you notice about the speed of the waves?

F. What happens to the distance between the waves when you increase the rate at which you generate them?

Figure 7.7 *Practice generating waves. Try to make the waves as straight as possible. Single waves can be generated by slowly rolling the dowel backward and forward a few millimeters (mm) in the water. Make closely spaced waves by rapidly rolling the dowel a few mm backward and forward. The waves can be best observed by looking below the tray where they are projected onto the paper. Do it gently. Don't splash water out of the tray.*

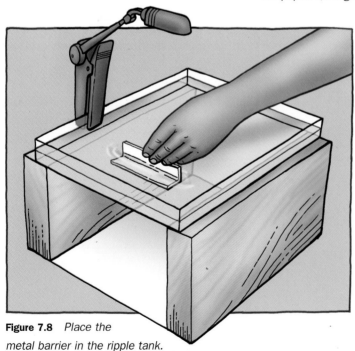

Figure 7.8 *Place the metal barrier in the ripple tank. Direct waves at the barrier.*

8. Place the metal barrier in the ripple tank as shown in Figure 7.8. Direct waves at the barrier.

G. Use a diagram and words to record any evidence of shadow formation.

9. Review your procedures, observations, and conclusions as you did in Inquiry 7.1 by using the discussion questions under Step 6 in that inquiry.

10. Dismantle your ripple tank. Pour the water out of the tray. Dry the tray with a paper towel. Return all the materials to the box.

REFLECTING ON WHAT YOU'VE DONE

With your group, discuss how the behavior of ball bearings and water waves compares with the behavior of light.

A. Summarize your ideas in Table 1 on Student Sheet 7.2.

B. From your observations, do you think light behaves like waves, like particles, or sometimes like both waves and particles? Record your own ideas about this. Be prepared to share your ideas with the class.

WAVE OR PARTICLE MODELS

Many of the characteristics of light can be modeled as waves and as particles. Scientists find both models useful in understanding the behavior of light. These models allow scientists to discuss and think about light as electromagnetic wave energy or as particles (more accurately, as packets of energy called photons). Often scientists use both of these ideas in thinking about the nature of light. You will learn more about each of these ideas as you work through this module.

© RDF/VISUALS UNLIMITED

Seeing Waves

Energy from a stone dropped into the water is transmitted through this pool of water as waves.

When most people think of waves, they think of waves in water. For example, you have probably seen waves breaking on a beach or waves made by someone jumping into a swimming pool.

Think about the waves produced when you throw a stone into a pool of still water. When the stone hits the water, you see a splash. Then a wave, or waves, radiates out from the point of impact. Where did the energy come from to make that wave?

All waves carry energy. A surfer riding a giant roller off the coast of California is using energy that may have been carried thousands

of kilometers across the ocean—energy gained from the wind of a storm on the shores of another continent. As a wave moves through the ocean, it does not carry water with it. Instead, the water moves up and down in a circular motion as the wave passes through it. When the wave meets a distant shore, it breaks, transferring its energy to the shore. Sometimes this causes disastrous results. The large waves of hurricanes and other storms often destroy waterfront property.

Waves Are All Around Us

You may not recognize them, but you see

waves all the time. Think about flags flying on a windy day. If you look closely at the way they flap in the wind, you can usually see waves passing along the fabric. The energy carried by the wave comes from the wind and travels along the cloth.

Other solid objects also show wave motion. Look at a field of grass on a windy day. Energy from the wind creates waves that are transmitted from plant to plant as they sway. The top of the grass creates

All waves transmit energy. The transfer of energy from ocean waves to the shore can be very destructive.

Waves are traveling along these flags.

Galloping Gertie Waves Goodbye

Would you like to drive across a bridge such as this? The Tacoma Narrows Bridge in Washington State was nicknamed "Galloping Gertie" because of wave action caused by even slight winds.

Eventually, on November 7, 1940, the Tacoma Narrows Bridge collapsed during moderate wind conditions. What do you think caused the bridge to fail?

the illusion of a "sea of grass." Tall buildings and bridges also sway in the wind as waves are transmitted through their structures. Earthquakes are transmitted by waves that travel through the ground. They can make buildings sway so much that they collapse.

Some waves are invisible. For example, sound is transmitted by waves that travel through the air or other matter. We hear sounds when the waves strike our eardrums and cause waves, or vibrations, in the eardrums.

The types of waves that have already been discussed are called mechanical waves. Mechanical waves can travel only through matter (that is, solids, liquids, and gases). Light also can travel through some matter—through glass or air, for example. Light is considered to be a type of wave, but not a mechanical wave. Light is an electromagnetic wave.

Unlike mechanical waves, electromagnetic waves can travel through a vacuum—the absence of matter. This means they can travel through the emptiness of space. All waves—both mechanical and electromagnetic—transmit energy and have certain other features in common. You will learn more about the nature of electromagnetic waves in Lesson 9. You also will have an opportunity to observe and measure some of the features of waves in that lesson. ◧

Music from this orchestra is transmitted as sound waves through the air to the ears of the audience.

Where Does Color Come From?

CORBIS/ROYALTY-FREE

When people enjoy the fall colors, what are their eyes detecting?

INTRODUCTION

In the fall, hundreds of thousands of tourists from all over the world go to New England to enjoy the changing colors of the leaves. Color is very important to them, but then it is important to everyone. Whether you are shopping for new clothes or a car, following a marked trail in the woods, or waiting for a red light to turn green, color matters. Color provides you with a great deal of useful information about your environment. The universe would certainly be a dull place without it. So, what is color? Why do things appear to be colored? Where does color come from? When you see color, what exactly are you seeing? In this lesson and the four that follow, you will try to answer some of these questions as you investigate color.

OBJECTIVES FOR THIS LESSON

Investigate where color comes from.

Discuss the appearance of the visible spectrum.

Getting Started

1. Collect the plastic box of materials. Take out the flashlight and triangular prism. Wait until you do Inquiry 8.1 to divide the rest of the materials between the pairs in your group.

2. Hold the triangular prism close to your eye and look around the room. Look through the window and at the lights in the classroom. Make sure your partner gets a turn. Discuss with your partner where you have seen this effect before.

3. After your teacher has darkened the room, shine the flashlight through the prism onto the ceiling. Try holding the prism at different distances from the flashlight and turning the prism around in the beam of light. What do you observe?

4. Discuss your observations with your group and with the class.

MATERIALS FOR LESSON 8

For your group
- 1 ray box
- 1 ray box lid
- 1 60-W clear halogen lightbulb
- 1 extension cord
- 1 bulb holder
- 2 narrow-slit ray box masks
- 2 no-slit ray box masks

For you and your lab partner
- 1 triangular prism
- 1 flashlight
- 2 D-cell batteries
- 1 white screen
- 2 plastic stands
- 1 box of colored pencils

Inquiry 8.1
Using a Triangular Prism To Examine White Light

PROCEDURE

1. Record your responses for this inquiry in your science notebook. There is no student sheet for this lesson.

2. Watch as your teacher demonstrates how to set up the ray box, prism, and white screen. Use Figure 8.1 as a guide as you follow the instructions to construct your ray box set out in the diagrams labeled a–d.

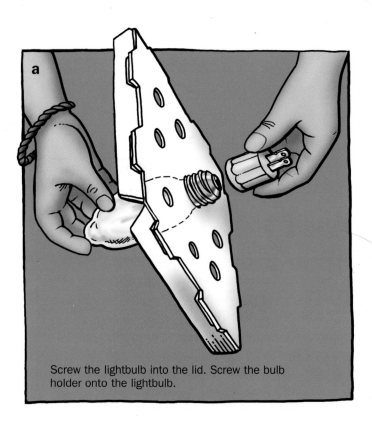

Screw the lightbulb into the lid. Screw the bulb holder onto the lightbulb.

SAFETY TIP

The lamp in the ray box gets hot. Allow it to cool for at least 5 minutes before handling the lightbulb.

Open the box. Put it on the table. Place the lid on the box. The flaps fit inside. Attach the extension cord to the bulb holder.

Figure 8.1 *Assembling the ray box. Two pairs can use each box.*

3. Place the triangular prism in the path of the light ray.

A. Draw what happens to the path of the light ray as it enters and leaves the prism.

Block off two opposite windows in the box with no-slit masks.

Slot two narrow-slit masks in the remaining windows. The bottom of the slit should be as close to the table as possible.

SAFETY TIP

Turn off the ray box immediately after you finish using it. Allow the ray box to cool.

Figure 8.2 *Can you get the colors you observed in "Getting Started" to form on your screen?*

4. Attach the plastic stands to the white screen. Place the screen in the path of the light ray leaving the prism. Rotate the prism and, if necessary, move the screen (as shown in Figure 8.2) until you get the same colors you observed in "Getting Started."

B. Use colored pencils to draw what you see.

C. Write down the names of the colors in the order in which you observe them.

D. Can you get the colors to appear on the screen in a different sequence?

5. Where do you think the colors you observed came from? Discuss your ideas with your partner. Here are some questions to consider:

What happened to the light rays when they first entered the prism?

Did all the colors leave the prism at the same place?

What did the prism do to the white light?

E. Write a paragraph explaining where you think the colors came from.

REFLECTING ON WHAT YOU'VE DONE

1. Scientists once thought that glass added colors to white light. What do you think of this hypothesis? How could you test it? Discuss this idea with your group. Be prepared to engage in a class discussion.

2. Read "The Impurity of White" and record your responses to A and B in your notebook.

A. What did Newton's experiments prove?

B. Write a paragraph summarizing his experiment.

The Impurity of White

For centuries the Western world had thought of white as the color of purity. The color white was associated with all that is pure and innocent. Along came a young English scientist, Isaac Newton (1642–1727), who changed people's ideas about the world of color forever. It was Newton who discovered in the 17th century that white light is not pure; it is a mixture of different colors.

Working in a darkened room, Newton experimented with a beam of light by allowing sunlight to shine into the room through a small hole in the wall. He then

All color comes from light, whether it is the colored beak of a spectacular bird like this penguin or the bright colors of clothing. All things that are colored reflect some of the colors that make up white light.

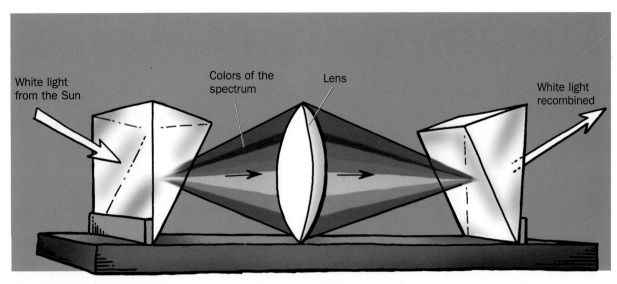

Newton used prisms and a lens to recombine the colors in white light. Sunlight came in from the left, was split into its spectrum, and then was recombined using a lens and a second, identical, upside-down prism.

passed this beam of light through a glass prism. The result was a line of different colors, which he projected onto a white screen. But this part of his experiment was not new.

Many people had already observed that white light can produce a line of colors that is called a spectrum. For thousands of years, people observed how colors were produced when sunlight shone through crystals or droplets of water.

Everyone recognized these colors were the same as those found in rainbows. Most people believed that pure white light from the Sun was changed or contaminated in some way when it passed through the crystals or water. But on that day in 1666, Newton took his experiment one step further. And what he discovered turned people's ideas about the world of color upside down.

Recombining the Spectrum

"What would happen," Newton wondered, "if I used another prism but turned it upside down with respect to the first? Then the colors pro-

duced by the first prism would shine into the second one." He tried out his idea. He used two prisms and a lens, as shown here.

The first prism produced a colored spectrum. The lens then focused the spectrum onto a second, identical, upside-down prism. The spectrum left the second prism as a ray of white light. Newton could think of only one logical explanation. Instead of contaminating white light, the first prism split it into the different colors that make up white light. The second prism recombined those colors back into white light. White was not pure, but instead a mixture of color.

At the time many people found Newton's discovery very disturbing. It took quite a few years before they could accept that white was not a pure color. In fact, it was the least pure of all colors. At first, there was much opposition to his discovery. However, Newton's experiment was easily repeated. By the end of the 17th century, it was widely accepted that Newton's explanation of the spectrum produced by white light was the correct one. ☐

NORTHWIND PICTURE ARCHIVES

Newton used a glass prism and a beam of sunlight to produce a spectrum. Where did the colors in this spectrum come from?

CORBIS IMAGES, PICTUREQUEST

Explaining a Rainbow

White light is made up of the many colors of visible light—light we can see. A prism splits white light into these colors. It does this by bending the various colors of light at slightly different angles as they enter the prism. This causes the colors to spread out, splitting them apart.

You have seen these colors before. They are the same ones that make up a rainbow. But a rainbow does not contain a prism, so how are the colors of a rainbow made?

A rainbow is not made from a single prism like the one you used, but a summer shower does contain billions of raindrops. As sunlight enters each drop, it bends, bounces off the back of the raindrop, and bends again when it leaves. As you can see from the illustration, bending the sunlight makes the white light split—just like a prism bends and splits white light. The raindrops that produce a rainbow behave a bit like billions of tiny prisms.

But why does a rainbow look like big bands of color? Inside each raindrop, each color of white light is bent a different amount. Because the raindrops are in different positions in the sky, they bend different colors to your eye. The appearance of the rainbow depends on the raindrops that make it up. Larger droplets separate the colors well, making the colors of the rainbow appear more distinct. When the droplets are very small, the colors can overlap and the rainbow becomes almost white and more difficult to see.

Although a rainbow appears to be an arc stretching across the sky, it actually forms a full circle. To an observer standing on Earth's surface, the rest of the circle is hidden below the horizon. There is no end to a rainbow!

Colored bows can be seen wherever sunlight strikes water droplets at certain angles. Many waterfalls produce rainbows in their spray. Sometimes bows of color ("dew bows") can be seen on early morning dew. ◻

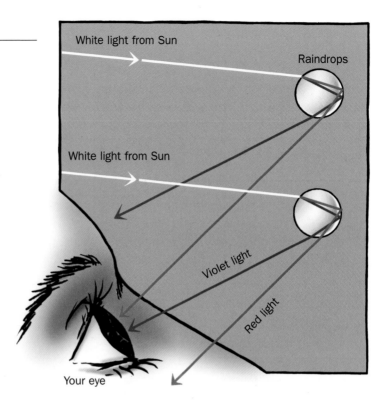

Raindrops split white light into the colors that make it up. Raindrops in different positions send different colors to the eye of someone looking at the rainbow. Red light is seen from raindrops at an angle of 42 ° to the horizon, violet light from raindrops at an angle of 40 °. The other colors of the rainbow are seen at angles between 40 ° and 42 °. This is why rainbows are only visible to the observer as a narrow curved band in the sky. Using this diagram, think about what direction—up or down—you would have to look to see red light or violet light.

You don't need rain to make a rainbow. The spray from a waterfall can produce its own rainbow.

Which Colors Are in a Rainbow?

A rainbow has many colors. How many exactly? Some people suggest there are only seven: red, orange, yellow, green, blue, indigo, and violet. They even have a nonsense phrase to help them remember them—ROY G BIV. How many colors did you detect using your prism? Were there only seven? Could you see a greenish blue or a yellowish green? In fact, there are millions of colors in a rainbow. It's just that we have names for only a few of them!

Can you see in a rainbow or through a prism all the colors our eyes can perceive? Try looking for magenta or brown.

Color, Wavelength, and the Wider Electromagnetic Spectrum

What property of light enables us to distinguish between the colors on these cards?

INTRODUCTION

In the previous lesson, you discovered that white light could be split to produce a visible spectrum of different colors. What is it about light that makes it appear to be different colors? What property of light allows your eyes to distinguish between red and blue or between yellow and orange? In this lesson, you will use one of the models for light from Lesson 7—the wave model—to help explain what your eyes detect when you see color. You also will discuss and investigate the existence and behavior of "invisible light." This "invisible light" is the part of the electromagnetic spectrum that exists outside the range of your vision.

OBJECTIVES FOR THIS LESSON

Model light waves of different colors.

Discuss evidence for an invisible spectrum.

Investigate the behavior of infrared.

Getting Started

1. Can you use a piece of beaded chain to make waves? As you and your partner experiment with the chain, think about these questions:

What do you have to do to the chain to make waves?

What does the wave transmit down the chain?

2. In a class discussion, share your approach to making waves and any observations you may have.

MATERIALS FOR LESSON 9

For you
1 copy of Student Sheet 9.2: Constructing the Spectrum
1 pair of scissors

For you and your lab partner
1 piece of beaded chain
1 meterstick
  Glue

Inquiry 9.1
Measuring Different Wavelengths

PROCEDURE

1. You are going to examine and measure the waves you make with your chain. To do this, you will need to freeze the motion of the chain on a flat surface. Work with class members to determine which method of making waves best allows you to freeze the motion of the chain.

2. Use the method the class selects to make waves. Stop shaking the chain abruptly. In your science notebook, draw the pattern formed by the chain. Do not move your chain.

3. Read "Measuring a Wave." Measure the wavelength (in mm) of the wave shown in the diagram in "Measuring a Wave." Record your measurement in your notebook.

4. Now measure and record the wavelength of the wave you made with the chain (see Figure 9.1). Your wave may not be the exact shape of the wave shown in the diagram. You may find it useful to measure a few wavelengths on your chain and take their average (mean) wavelength.

5. Shake the chain faster than you did in Step 2. Abruptly stop shaking it. Draw the pattern formed by the chain. Do not move the chain. In your notebook, answer the following questions:

   A. What is the difference between the two wave patterns?

   B. What is the wavelength of the new wave?

   C. What happened to the wavelength of the chain when you shook the chain faster?

6. Shake the chain again, starting slowly and then speeding up. Record what happens to the frequency of waves in the chain. (Remember: Frequency is the number of waves that pass a certain point every second.)

   D. What is the relationship between the wavelength of your waves and their frequency?

   E. Which wavelengths of your chain carry the most energy?

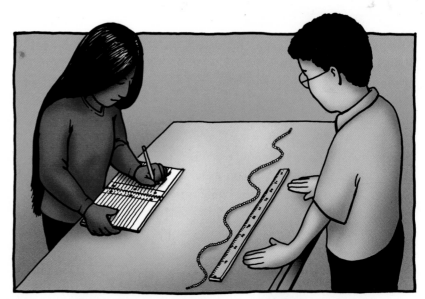

Figure 9.1 *What is the wavelength of the wave you made with the chain?*

MEASURING A WAVE

Waves can vary in length and height. The distance between the crests (or the troughs) of two adjacent waves is the wavelength of the wave. The distance from the midpoint of the wave to its crest is the amplitude of the wave.

The number of waves that pass a certain point during a specific time—usually a second—is called the frequency of the wave and is measured in Hertz (Hz). With light rays, the speed of the light—the rate at which the waves move along—depends on what substance (or material) the light waves are traveling through. Light travels slightly slower in air than in a vacuum, and its exact speed through air depends on the density of the air. However, because light travels at a constant speed through a vacuum or any one material, frequency and wavelength are related to one another. Remember, the shorter the wavelength, the higher the frequency.

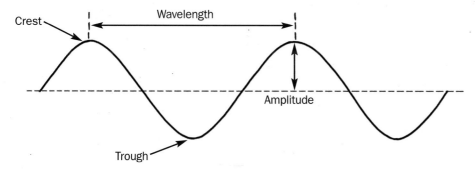

The distance between two crests, or two troughs, of adjacent waves is called the wavelength. The distance from the midpoint of the wave to its crest is the amplitude of the wave.

Inquiry 9.2
Constructing the Spectrum

PROCEDURE

1. Read "Color and Wavelength."

COLOR AND WAVELENGTH

You have been modeling light waves using your chain. But what does this have to do with color? Our eyes can detect different wavelengths of light. Our eyes and brain perceive these different wavelengths as color. We cannot see all the wavelengths of electromagnetic radiation—some are invisible. We see only those wavelengths that range from about 400 to 800 nanometers (a nanometer is one billionth of a meter (1×10^{-9} m), so these wavelengths are very tiny).

2. In this inquiry you will construct a model of the visible spectrum by identifying some waves and drawing other waves in the order they appear in the visible spectrum. Remember that red light has the longest wavelength and violet has the shortest in the visible spectrum.

A. On the first page of Student Sheet 9.2: Constructing the Spectrum are drawings of waves that represent red, green, and blue light. Identify each of these waves.

Cut them out and attach each to the appropriate row in Table 1 (on the second page of the student sheet).

B. Use a pencil to draw the waves for orange, yellow, indigo, and violet in the appropriate rows of Table 1.

3. Read "Infrared and Ultraviolet" to learn about waves that are shorter and waves that are longer than those of visible light.

INFRARED AND ULTRAVIOLET

The spectrum of visible light is part of a much larger spectrum of waves called the electromagnetic spectrum. The electromagnetic spectrum contains wavelengths that are much longer and wavelengths that are much shorter than those of visible light. Most wavelengths of electromagnetic waves are invisible to the human eye. For example, infrared is invisible electromagnetic radiation, with wavelengths a little longer than red light. Ultraviolet is invisible electromagnetic radiation, with wavelengths slightly shorter than violet light.

C. Identify the wave in Table 1 that represents ultraviolet and the wave that represents infrared. Correctly label these waves on the table.

4. Read more about the invisible electromagnetic spectrum in "The Hidden Spectrum."

Inquiry 9.3
Looking Outside the Visible Spectrum

PROCEDURE

1. Your teacher will show you an everyday device that produces invisible infrared. Work with your group to devise a series of simple experiments to compare the behavior of the infrared produced by this device with the behavior of visible light. Record your ideas in your notebook.

2. Discuss your ideas with the class. When the class has agreed on a series of simple experiments, design a table in your notebook to record the results of these experiments and compare the behavior of infrared to the behavior of visible light.

3. Your teacher will ask you to either try some of the experiments at home or have different groups of students demonstrate them in class. Record in your table the results of any experiments that are conducted.

4. Discuss the results of the experiments with other students. *Do you think that infrared behaves like visible light?*

Is this dog an expert on using the invisible electromagnetic spectrum?

REFLECTING ON WHAT YOU'VE DONE

1. Draw a wave in your notebook. Label the following features on the wave: wavelength, amplitude, trough, and crest.

2. Answer the following questions in your notebook:

A. In the wave model for light, what feature of the wave determines how your eyes sense the color of a particular wave of light?

B. In the visible spectrum, your eyes detect the longest wavelength as what color?

C. In the visible spectrum, your eyes detect the shortest wavelength as what color?

D. Which type of electromagnetic radiation lies directly below the red end of the visible spectrum?

E. Which type of electromagnetic radiation lies directly above the violet end of the visible spectrum?

3. Discuss your answers to these questions with the class.

The Hidden Spectrum

In 1800, William Herschel discovered infrared light. He thought he had discovered heat rays. It took almost 50 years for scientists to determine that the invisible infrared had characteristics similar to those of visible light.

In 1800, the famous astronomer William Herschel (1738–1822) began to study sunspots. To protect his eyes, he added special filters to his telescope. He pointed the telescope at the Sun and was able to see sunspots very clearly.

But after a few minutes, he ran into a problem. His telescope got too hot to use. Why was this happening? Was there a link between the temperature of his telescope and light? He decided to conduct some experiments to try to answer these questions.

William Herschel used this prism to split sunlight. He used thermometers to measure the increases in temperature produced by different colors. He also discovered that beyond the red end of the visible spectrum was an invisible form of radiation that produced an even greater increase in temperature.

In one experiment, Herschel tried to find out which color in white light produced the most heat when it hit a surface. He used a prism to split white light into its different colors. He put a thermometer in each line of colored light and measured the increase in temperature produced by each color. He discovered that red light produced the most heat. He then put a thermometer just outside the red end of the spectrum. Here no light was visible, but to his surprise the thermometer got even hotter. He had discovered an invisible form of light. Herschel incorrectly thought he had discovered heat rays. This invisible light was later called infrared. Were there other types of invisible light? The search was on!

Widening the Search

Johann Wilhelm Ritter (1776–1810), a German scientist, heard about Herschel's discovery. He decided to use a light-sensitive chemical to search for other types of invisible light. He used the chemical to test for light at the violet end of the visible spectrum. He found another invisible form of light and named it ultraviolet.

Soon the idea of a whole range, or spectrum, of radiation began to grow. Scientists realized that visible light made up only a tiny part of a much wider electromagnetic spectrum. The idea of an electromagnetic spectrum fit neatly with the emerging idea that light was a form of wave energy. Different colors and types of light belonged to the same electromagnetic spectrum. They simply had different wavelengths.

Many types of electromagnetic waves have been identified. Wavelengths can be as long as tens of kilometers (radio waves) and as short as 0.000000000000001 millimeters—10^{-15} meters— (gamma rays). □

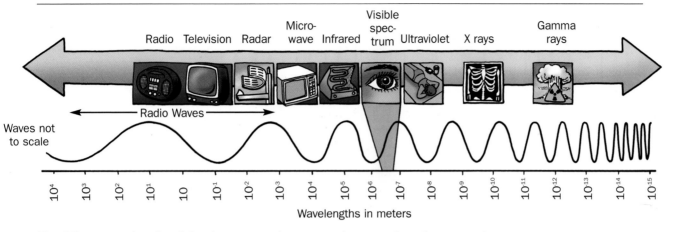

The different wavelengths of the electromagnetic spectrum have a variety of names and uses.

Tuning In

Have you ever tried tuning a radio? Have you wondered about those numbers on a digital display or scale? And what's all this about AM and FM?

The numbers refer to the frequency of the electromagnetic waves—radio waves—you are tuning into. AM and FM refer to groups or bands of radio frequencies. AM frequencies are around 1 million waves per second or 1 megahertz (MHz). Waves in the FM band are about 100 times shorter, with a frequency of 100 MHz. Remember, the shorter the wave, the higher the frequency (the number of waves that pass a certain point every second).

Which frequency do you tune into most frequently?

VIEWING THE WORLD AND BEYOND IN INFRARED

This infrared image uses color to show where infrared is given off. The red areas show parts of the face giving off the most infrared. This image shows a hot face but cool sunglasses!

INFRARED PROCESSING AND ANALYSIS CENTER, CALTECH/JET PROPULSION LABORATORY

Infrared may be invisible, but it can still be detected. Hot objects give off infrared. Hold your hands near a heater and they will soon warm up. When the infrared released by the heater strikes our hands, the infrared is transformed back into heat. By using special film or special electronic cameras, you can view the world in infrared. One such device could be looking at your school right now. In orbit around Earth are satellites designed to view Earth in infrared. The images they collect can provide information on the condition of crops, pollution, or the temperature of the oceans.

Weather satellites take images in infrared. Meteorologists use these images to record the temperature of air masses moving across the planet. These images also can record the temperature of the clouds inside giant storms.

Infrared detectors in space also look away from Earth. Many regions of the universe cannot be seen with optical telescopes. These regions are hidden by clouds of gas

This infrared image shows the Amazon Basin in South America. It can be used to identify areas where the rainforest has been cut down.

In this infrared image of hurricane Linda, the purple areas in the center of the storm show the warmest air and clouds.

Rainforest destruction, such as that caused by this fire, can be monitored using Earth-orbiting satellites. Some of these satellites look at Earth using infrared detectors.

and dust. However, infrared can pass through these clouds. So it is possible to see through these clouds by using orbiting infrared observatories such as the Infrared Astronomical Satellite (known as IRAS). IRAS gives astronomers a different perspective on the universe. With it, they can look into the center of our own galaxy. Infrared can be used to detect objects much cooler than stars. Astronomers also use infrared to look for planetary systems other than our own solar system.

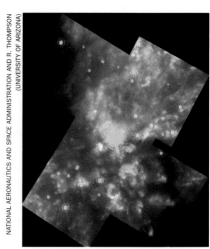

Visible light photos of the Orion Nebula look like a glowing cloud containing a few stars (as on the left). The picture on the right was taken using infrared wavelengths from part of the Orion Nebula and reveals much more information about its structure. Infrared allows astronomers to see through the clouds of dust and gas that usually obscure this view.

Using Infrared Closer to Home

Back here on Earth, seeing in infrared gives us a new view of our world—even a new view of ourselves. Look at the human face in infrared. You can see the different temperatures of skin. The human face begins to look quite different.

Looking at objects in infrared provides engineers with useful information. For example, they can use infrared detectors to discover how buildings lose heat. This helps them design buildings that are more energy efficient. They also can use the detectors to check electrical systems for overheating that could cause fires. Computer makers use infrared sensors to look for hot spots on circuit boards. Automakers use these sensors to check that car engines are running properly. Railroads use infrared sensors to spot overheated wheels on railroad cars.

By making the invisible visible, infrared photography and detection allow people to see a world that previously was hidden from view. □

An infrared photograph shows that this house has a well-insulated roof (blue-green areas), but loses much of its heat through its walls and windows (orange areas).

QUESTION

What is another use of infrared? Use the Internet or an encyclopedia to research one additional use of infrared in detail.

Burning Our Biggest Organ

STOCKBYTE/PICTUREQUEST

Is this boy endangering his body's largest organ?

Put on your hat, and don't forget the sunscreen. Yes, it's one of those hot summer days, ideal for having fun in or on the water. But spending the morning tubing on a river or swimming at the local pool could cause you to severely burn the largest organ in your body!

No, it's not your liver; it's your skin. The cells that make up the skin all work together to perform a specific function. The skin's job is to separate the inside of your body from the outside world, and the skin does its job well. Outside the body, there are many harmful things. One of these is electromagnetic radiation. Visible light is fairly harmless, but some types of invisible electromagnetic radiation can be very damaging. For example, ultraviolet radiation (UV) causes sunburn.

The Sun produces lots of UV of a variety of different wavelengths. Luckily, most UV is absorbed high in the atmosphere and never reaches Earth's surface. The layer of the atmosphere that absorbs UV is called the ozone layer (see "Ozone and the Ozone Layer" sidebar).

Tanning is the skin's natural reaction to UV. When skin tans, it produces a brown substance called melanin. Cells deep in the skin produce melanin, which acts as a protective barrier by absorbing harmful radiation. In light-skinned people, these cells are less active. People with darker skins produce more melanin than people with lighter skin. In fact, the darkness of people's skins is mainly an indicator of the amount of melanin they produce. Different skin colors are probably the result of adaptation to different levels of UV at different parts of the globe.

Sunburn is the body's reaction to damage caused by UV. Overexposure to UV can kill cells or damage parts of cells, including DNA. The body reacts as it would to an ordinary burn or other skin damage—but slower. A few hours after exposure to the Sun, the skin becomes red, inflamed, and painful. This is why it is easy to get sunburned and not know it until even the following day!

A minor sunburn often heals after a few days. (A bad sunburn, like any burn, can kill.) But repeatedly burning one part of the skin can cause skin cancer. That's why it is important to protect your skin from UV. One way is simply to cover up—wear a wide-brimmed hat and long-sleeved shirt and long pants.

Another way to get some protection from UV is to use a sunscreen. Sunscreens work in two ways. Some sunscreens look white; they simply reflect UV. Others absorb the UV. They work just like our natural skin protector, melanin. If you look at a bottle of sunscreen, you'll notice it is labeled with a Sun Protection Factor (SPF). The higher the SPF, the more effective the sunscreen.

So the next time you are out in the Sun, slip on a hat and slap on the sunscreen! Your skin will thank you. ☐

Dark skin provides better protection from UV. Different skin colors offer different levels of protection.

Ozone and the Ozone Layer

The ozone layer of Earth's atmosphere protects us from most of the Sun's UV radiation. Ozone—a type of oxygen—is able to absorb UV. A layer of ozone about 24 kilometers (15 miles) up in the atmosphere shields Earth. The amount of ozone present high in the atmosphere varies naturally over time. However, in the last 30 years scientists have found that human activity is slowly destroying the ozone layer. Pollution, such as some chemicals used in old aerosol cans, refrigerators, and air conditioners, gets into the ozone layer and reacts with and destroys ozone. Scientists have observed big "holes" appearing in the ozone layer where the levels of ozone are very low. The largest of these holes is in the Southern Hemisphere. Scientists also have observed declining levels of ozone in the ozone layer over the whole globe.

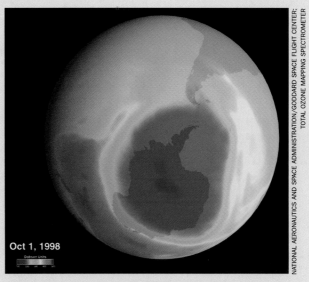

Oct 1, 1998

Dobson Units

NATIONAL AERONAUTICS AND SPACE ADMINISTRATION/GODDARD SPACE FLIGHT CENTER; TOTAL OZONE MAPPING SPECTROMETER

We are protected from some UV by the ozone layer. However, pollution has reduced the amount of ozone in the ozone layer making it less effective. Now a large hole (shown here in blue) has appeared in the layer over part of the Southern Hemisphere.

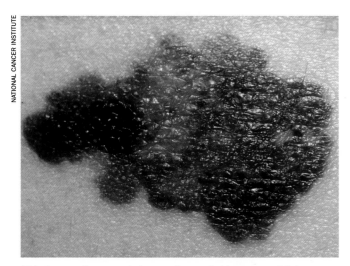

NATIONAL CANCER INSTITUTE

This is a melanoma. It is one form of skin cancer. Melanomas can be caused by overexposure to UV.

CORBIS/ROYALTY-FREE

Ouch! Sunburn can damage the skin. Tanning indicates the skin has been overexposed to UV. A bad sunburn like that shown here can be very painful, and a very bad sunburn can be life threatening.

10
Examining Spectra

These students are using spectroscopes like the one you are going to make to observe different light sources.

COURTESY OF DAVID MARSLAND/© NSRC

INTRODUCTION

Electromagnetic radiation from the Sun provides Earth with light and heat. That same electromagnetic energy also provides scientists with information about the nature of the Sun itself. You have already discovered that white light, including light from the Sun, can be split into many colors or wavelengths. But did you know that by examining the spectrum of sunlight it is possible to determine what the Sun is made of. In fact, studying the spectrum produced by any object—whether a distant giant star or a tiny candle flame—can provide us with a great deal of useful information about it. The study of spectra (spectra is the plural of spectrum) is called spectroscopy. In this lesson, you build an instrument called a spectroscope. You will use your spectroscope to investigate spectra from different light sources.

OBJECTIVES FOR THIS LESSON

Build a spectroscope.

Use the spectroscope to examine light from different sources.

Discuss how spectroscopy is used.

Getting Started

1. Hold the small square of plastic by its edges. Take care not to get any fingerprints on its surface. Look through it at the lights in the classroom. Discuss your observations and the following questions with your partner:

What do you observe?

Have you seen anything similar to this before?

What does this piece of plastic do to white light?

2. Read "How the Piece of Plastic Separates Light."

HOW THE PIECE OF PLASTIC SEPARATES LIGHT

You have been given a piece of plastic called a diffraction grating. Look closely at its surface. It is covered by thousands of regularly spaced, parallel tiny scratches. These scratches bend light waves that pass through the plastic. This bending process is called diffraction. The amount a wave bends depends on its wavelength. This plastic diffraction grating can therefore be used to separate light made up of more than one wavelength—white light, for example. As the different wavelengths in a mixture of visible light bend by different amounts, they separate. These separated wavelengths can be seen as a spectrum of the different colors that make up the mixture.

MATERIALS FOR LESSON 10

For you
1 copy of Student Sheet 10.1: Using a Simple Spectroscope
1 cardboard tube
1 square of aluminum foil
1 square of black paper with a square hole

For you and your lab partner
1 pair of scissors
1 metric ruler
1 box of colored pencils
  Masking tape

Inquiry 10.1
Using a Simple
Spectroscope

PROCEDURE

1. One member of your group should collect the plastic box of materials. Divide the materials between the pairs in your group.

2. Each member of your group will make a spectroscope. Use Figure 10.1 as a guide as you follow the instructions to construct your spectroscope outlined in the diagrams labeled a–i.

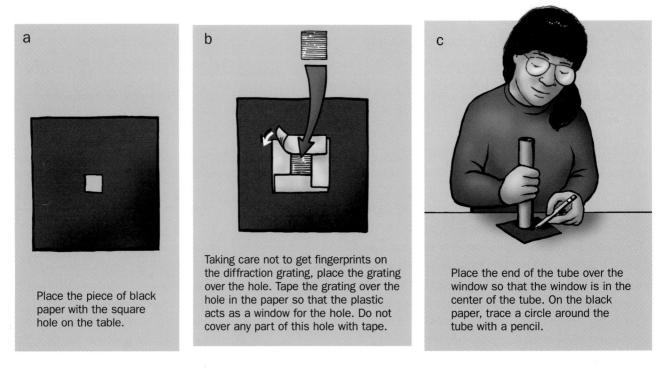

a

Place the piece of black paper with the square hole on the table.

b

Taking care not to get fingerprints on the diffraction grating, place the grating over the hole. Tape the grating over the hole in the paper so that the plastic acts as a window for the hole. Do not cover any part of this hole with tape.

c

Place the end of the tube over the window so that the window is in the center of the tube. On the black paper, trace a circle around the tube with a pencil.

Figure 10.1 *Use these diagrams labeled a–i as a guide to help you construct your spectroscope.*

d

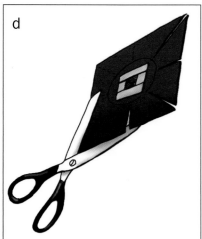

Carefully make cuts in the black paper from the edge of the paper inward to *just outside* the edge of the circle you have drawn.

e

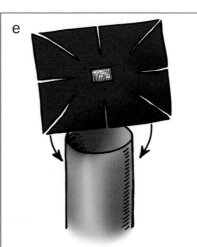

Turn the paper around so that the taped side (with the diffraction grating) faces the open end of the tube.

f

Make sure the diffraction grating window is centered over the opening of the tube. Keep the black paper as flat a possible over the end of the tube and tape it to the end of the tube as shown.

g

Cut a 3-cm length of masking tape. Stick it onto the center of the piece of aluminum foil.

h

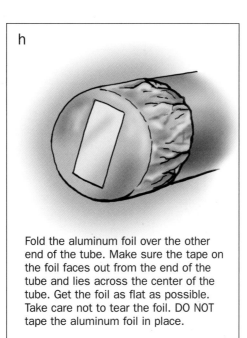

Fold the aluminum foil over the other end of the tube. Make sure the tape on the foil faces out from the end of the tube and lies across the center of the tube. Get the foil as flat as possible. Take care not to tear the foil. DO NOT tape the aluminum foil in place.

i

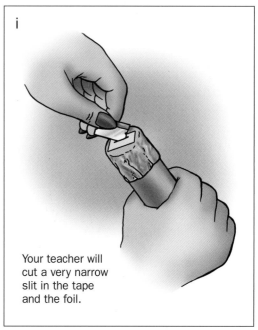

Your teacher will cut a very narrow slit in the tape and the foil.

3. Your spectroscope is now complete. Compare it to the one in Figure 10.2.

4. Look through your spectroscope at daylight outside the window. The foil end of the tube should be facing the window (see Figure 10.3). Rotate the foil until you observe the widest spectrum.

A. Use colored pencils to record in the second column of Table 1 on Student Sheet 10.1: Using a Simple Spectroscope exactly what you observe through your spectroscope. Write any observations or comments you have in the third column of the table.

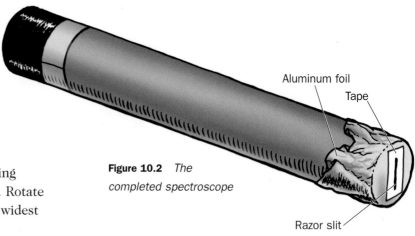

Figure 10.2 *The completed spectroscope*

Aluminum foil

Tape

Razor slit

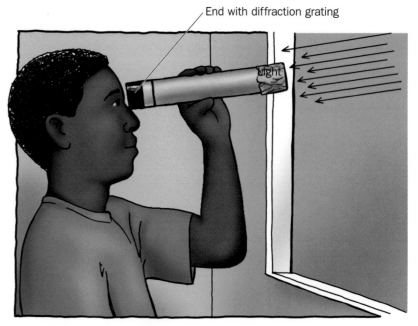

End with diffraction grating

Light

Figure 10.3 *Use your spectroscope to observe daylight.*

SAFETY TIP

Do not look directly at the Sun through your spectroscope, a telescope, or with your bare eyes. It could permanently damage your eyes.

5. Point your spectroscope at an incandescent lightbulb. Record the spectrum and your observations and comments in Table 1. Make sure you record exactly what you see.

6. Point your spectroscope at a fluorescent lightbulb. Look carefully at the spectrum. Record the spectrum and your observations and comments in Table 1. Discuss your observations with your group.

B. Write a short paragraph comparing the spectra from these three light sources—daylight, incandescent lightbulb, and compact flourescent lightbulb.

7. Your teacher will show you a number of other light sources. Observe each carefully. Record their spectra and your observations and comments in the remaining rows of Table 1.

8. Don't dismantle your spectroscope. Write your name on it. You will be using it again in the next lesson.

REFLECTING ON WHAT YOU'VE DONE

1. Discuss with your group and then answer the following questions on the student sheet:

A. What happens to light when it passes through your spectroscope?

B. What can you now say about the spectra from various light sources?

C. How could this information be useful?

2. Read more about how spectroscopes are used in "The Science of Spectroscopy."

SAFETY TIP

Do not touch any of these light sources. They get very hot and can cause painful burns.

The Science of
SPECTROSCOPY

A closer look at the solar spectrum shows that it has may different wavelengths and also some gaps that show up as black lines. This spectrum reveals information about the composition of the Sun. This spectrum has been cut up and displayed this way so that it can fit on the page.

All matter consists of one or more chemical elements. When heated to a high enough temperature, all elements glow—they emit light. You may have noticed that various light sources have different colors when viewed with your eyes. For example, fluorescent tubes in your classroom look white, and neon tubes glow red. When you look at light emitted from one of these tubes through a spectroscope, you see the spectrum for that light source. This spectrum is an *emission* spectrum. Every element has a unique emission spectrum.

Substances may also absorb light. For example, if white light is shone through a gas, the gas will absorb some of the wavelengths of the light. If you look through a spectroscope at the spectrum leaving the gas, you will see dark lines where you would expect some of the

At first glance, the spectrum of sunlight looks continuous.

Light from distant stars can be very faint. Astronomers use sensitive electronic devices, similar to those found in video cameras, to record the spectra of dim distant objects.

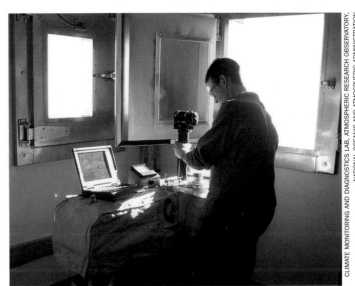

Spectroscopy is used by scientists to analyze the composition of unknown substances inside and beyond the laboratory. This scientist working at the South Pole is using a device called a spectrophotometer, which uses light to find out the composition and density of the ozone layer.

wavelengths should be. These wavelengths were absorbed by the gas. This spectrum is called an *absorption* spectrum. Different substances produce different emission and absorption spectra. Both types of spectra can be used to identify the composition of substances. The use of a spectroscope to analyze matter using its emission spectrum is called spectroscopy.

Spectroscopy is a useful tool for chemists. Just as a fingerprint can identify a person, a spectrum can identify a substance. Scientists use spectroscopy to find out the composition of substances.

Analyzing Stars

Spectroscopy has uses well beyond studying substances found on Earth and in its atmosphere. Astronomers can use a spectroscope attached to a telescope to determine the composition of the universe. Consider the spectrum of the closest star to Earth, the Sun. We often think of this glowing ball of gas as producing a continuous spectrum, running from red to violet.

But what happens when sunlight is passed through a sensitive spectroscope? More lines of color can be seen. Look closely at the picture behind the title. You will also see many dark lines. Some of these lines indicate that the gases in the outer layers of the Sun have absorbed some of the wavelengths in sunlight. The missing colors provide information on the composition of these gases.

Spectroscopy can provide information about stars beyond their composition. Astronomers can use this tool to estimate how hot stars or other objects are, and even how fast they are traveling. ☐

11

Looking at Colors

Why do the flowers in the picture appear to be colored? What color would they be if there were no light?

INTRODUCTION

In Lesson 10, you used your spectroscope to observe colors emitted from light sources. Do you think the source of the light is the only thing that determines the colors that make up light that reaches your eye? Why do many objects appear to be colored when illuminated by white light? Why does the color of these objects appear to change when you look at them through transparent colored glass or plastic? In this lesson, you will use your eyes and spectroscopes to try to find the answers to these questions.

OBJECTIVES FOR THIS LESSON

Examine some colored objects and explain why they are colored.

Use a spectroscope to examine light before and after it passes through transparent colored sheets.

Predict and observe the appearance of different colors when they are viewed through transparent colored sheets.

Getting Started

1. One member of your group should collect the plastic box of materials and divide the materials between the pairs in your group.

2. Look at the transparent colored sheets and colored pencils you have been given. Discuss with your group why these objects are colored. Be prepared to share your ideas with the class.

MATERIALS FOR LESSON 11

For you
1 copy of Student Sheet 11.1: Looking at Spectra Through Transparent Colored Sheets
1 copy of Student Sheet 11.2: Looking at Colors Through Filters
1 spectroscope

For you and your lab partner
Transparent colored sheets (red, green, and blue)
Colored pencils (red, green, and blue)

Inquiry 11.1
Looking at Spectra Through Transparent Colored Sheets

PROCEDURE

1. Use your spectroscope to observe white light before and after it passes through each of the colored sheets.

   A. Record your observations on Student Sheet 11.1: Looking at Spectra Through Transparent Colored Sheets, in a table of your own design.

2. Discuss your observations with your partner. Below are some questions you may wish to consider:

   Is the spectrum observed through the colored sheets the same as the spectrum for white light?

   Are more or fewer colors visible when you look through the colored sheets?

   What do the colored sheets do to white light?

   B. Write a short paragraph explaining your observations.

3. Sometimes transparent colored sheets are called color filters.

   C. Why do you think the transparent colored sheets are called color filters?

4. Write a short answer to the following question:

   D. What do red filters do to white light?

Inquiry 11.2
Looking at Colors Through Filters

PROCEDURE

1. Select the red, green, and blue colored pencils.

   A. In the first column of Table 1 on Student Sheet 11.2: Looking at Colors Through Filters, make a swatch of each color. White and black have been done for you. Label each swatch with the name of the color—use the color name written on the side of each colored pencil.

2. Look at the color swatches through the red filter *only*. Hold the filter about 10 cm above the color, as shown in Figure 11.1. Do not place it on the paper. Record the appearance of each color in the "Red" column of Table 1.

Figure 11.1 *Look through the red filter at the color swatches in Table 1. Hold the red filter about 10 cm above the surface of the paper.*

3. Predict how the same colors will appear under the green filter. Record your predictions in Table 1.

4. Test your predictions and record the results.

5. Repeat the same procedure using the blue filter.

6. Discuss your observations with your partner.

B. Did you notice any patterns in your results?

C. Can you explain these patterns? Record any ideas you may have.

REFLECTING ON WHAT YOU'VE DONE

1. Review your explanations and observations on Student Sheet 11.2 before recording your responses to A–D on the student sheet.

A. Draw a diagram that explains why a green object appears green when in white light.

B. Draw a diagram that explains why a green object under white light appears black when the object is viewed through a red filter.

2. What will you observe if white light passes through both a red filter and a blue filter?

C. Record your prediction and observations.

D. Explain your observations.

3. Read "Why Objects Look Colored." Think about the ideas you had at the beginning of the lesson about why objects were colored. Have these ideas changed?

Why Objects Look Colored

You can see objects because light travels from the objects to your eyes. Objects you can see are said to be visible. Light sources—luminous objects such as the Sun or a fluorescent light-bulb—are visible because they make visible light. But opaque, nonluminous objects do not make their own light. They are visible to your eyes because light from light sources bounces off them. In other words, light reflects off them.

Why do objects that reflect light appear to be colored? What, for example, happens when white light (made up of all colors of the visible spectrum) hits a yellow flower? The flower absorbs some colors in the white light and some—those that make up yellow—are reflected. You see this yellow light when some of it is reflected to your eyes.

Take another example. A red car looks red in white light because the car reflects only red light. The paint on the car absorbs the other

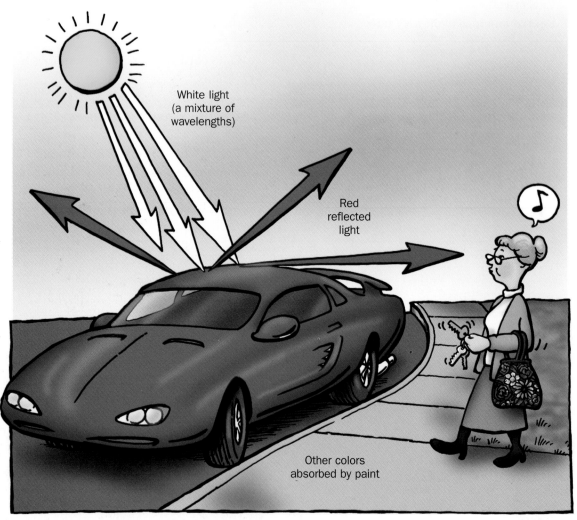

White light
(a mixture of
wavelengths)

Red
reflected
light

Other colors
absorbed by paint

Why does this car look red? The paint on the car absorbs most of the wavelengths in white light and reflects only those wavelengths that look red when detected by our eyes.

colors. Most objects reflect some colors or wavelengths of light and absorb others. Only silvered mirrors or white objects reflect all colors. Only completely black objects absorb all the colors of the spectrum. No light reflects from the surfaces of completely black objects, so no light from black objects reaches your eyes.

Some colors may also be produced by reflection of more than one wavelength of light. However, your eyes detect these wavelength mixtures as only one color. This concept may seem confusing, but it is something you have already discovered. You see the paper of this page as white, but you know that the light reflected from the paper to your eyes contains all the colors of the visible spectrum.

Filtering Light

There is a slightly different explanation for why an object observed through a filter appears to be the color you see. Filters allow only some wavelengths of light through them—they transmit some colors and remove (absorb) others—in other words, filters filter out some colors (or wavelengths). So when you look at a sheet of white paper through a red filter, the paper

The lenses of sunglasses are often gray. They reduce the intensity of the sunlight by filtering out some of the light. Gray lenses are used so that all colors the eyes detect are reduced equally. The sunglasses produce a scene that is dimmer but still normally colored.

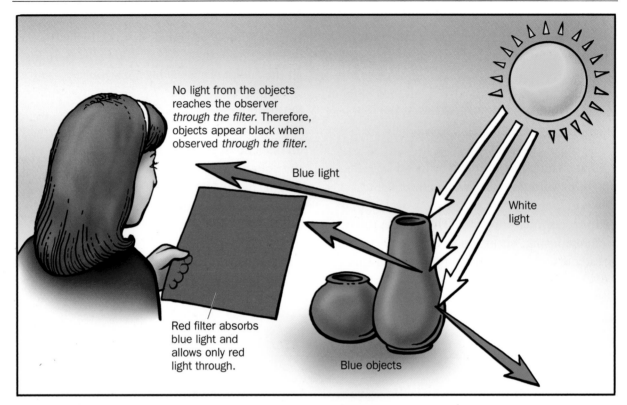

No light from the objects reaches the observer *through the filter.* Therefore, objects appear black when observed *through the filter.*

Blue light

White light

Red filter absorbs blue light and allows only red light through.

Blue objects

When viewed through a red filter, a blue object appears to be black. This is because the red filter absorbs the blue light reflected from the object.

appears red. It looks red because the filter absorbs all the colors, except red, from the white light the paper reflects. Only red light reflecting off the paper reaches your eyes. If you look at a blue object through the same filter, the object appears black. This is because the blue object reflects only blue light; none of the blue light reflected by the blue object can pass through the red filter. Therefore no light from the object reaches your eyes—the object appears to be black.

Objects or filters look colored because they absorb or subtract some colors from white light. This process of producing color by subtracting colors or wavelengths from white light is called color subtraction. When you paint a picture in art class or look at a colored illustration printed in this book, the color you see has been produced by color subtraction. In the next reader, you will learn more about how people developed the techniques of color printing. □

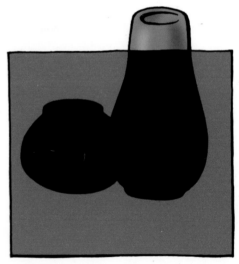

What the girl sees

PRINTING IN COLOR

Try to imagine a world without printed books, newspapers, or magazines. For many thousands of years people have used pictures and writing to communicate knowledge and ideas. But for most of this time, writing and pictures were not printed; they were copied by hand.

Buddhist monks in ancient China were the world's earliest expert printers. Over one thousand years ago, they used hand-carved blocks of wood to make thousands of copies of holy texts. The blocks were inked and then pressed onto silk and paper. The ancient Chinese were also the first to experiment with color in printed books.

While the Chinese already had developed their printing techniques, the Europeans were still hand-copying most of their books. Monks did most of this painstaking work. They then added color by hand in a process called illumination.

In monasteries throughout medieval Europe, books like these were copied and colored by hand.

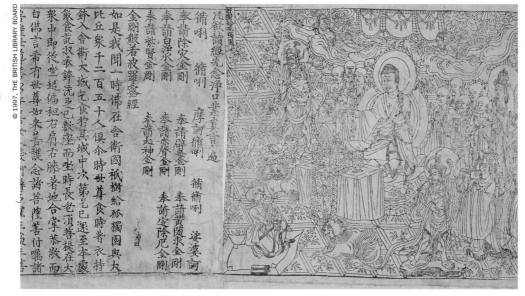

This Buddhist text is called the Diamond Sutra. It is the earliest dated printed book (A.D. 868). It was printed using carved wooden blocks.

The Beginning of Modern Printing

THE CLIP ART BOOK, CRESCENT BOOKS, AVENEL, NEW JERSEY, 1994

Printers in Germany's Rhine Valley adapted existing technology for pressing grapes (for wine) and olives (for oil) to mechanize the printing process.

COURTESY OF THE LIBRARY OF CONGRESS

LIBRARY OF CONGRESS, PRINTS & PHOTOGRAPHS DIVISION, LC-USZ62-104244

Johannes Gutenberg led a revolution in printing using movable type that made the process cheaper and faster. Printing became one of the first mass-production processes. The page shown is from a version of a Bible produced by Gutenberg.

Mechanizing the Printing Process

More than a thousand years after the invention of printing, the process became mechanized. The printing press was invented.

We don't know who invented the first printing press, but we do know that printing quickly became big business. In the 1450s, a German printer, Johannes Gutenberg, invented a method of making metal letters (called type) and casting individual metal letters in standard-sized molds. This speeded up the printing process. It became much cheaper to print books and pamphlets. However, pictures were still hand carved on wooden blocks or metal plates. These pictures were black and white, but were sometimes colored by hand.

As books became more available, more people learned to read. The demand for books increased. People wanted to read about far-off places and exciting new discoveries. They wanted their books to have more pictures, and they wanted these pictures to be colored. This drove the development of color printing.

Color for Everyone

The first successful method of large-scale color printing (called lithography) was invented near the end of the 19th century. Originally in lithography, designs were drawn on fine-grained stone with a special oily crayon or ink. The stone was then moistened with water. Because water and oil repel each other, the oily picture did not get wet—only the rest of the stone. Oily ink was then rolled onto the wet stone. Again because water and oil repel each other, the ink stuck only to the oily picture, not to the surrounding wet part of the stone. Paper was then pressed against the stone to make a print of the picture.

To print in different colors, multiple stones were used. One stone was used for each color. The paper had to go through the press many times to be pressed against each inked stone. The stones had to be carefully aligned so that the colors were printed in the correct place.

This process was faster than the illumination process done by hand, but it was still slow. At first, books printed by lithography were very expensive. However, with improved techniques and mechanization, the process eventually became inexpensive enough to print magazines and advertising circulars in color.

FROM THE COLLECTION OF MILL GROVE—AUDUBON WILDLIFE SANCTUARY

This picture is from a book by the naturalist and painter John James Audubon (1785–1851). Early editions of Audubon's books contained hand-tinted pictures. Illustrations from later editions, like the picture shown here, used an improved type of lithographic color printing called chromolithography.

Printing With Dots

Modern color printing is based on a similar process. These days, a picture is scanned electronically and broken into four separate images. Each image represents one of the colors—cyan, magenta, yellow, and black—that will make up the picture. The scanner also breaks up each colored image into dots. The more numerous the dots of a particular color, the stronger that color. Each image is then photographically transferred to a metal (not stone) printing plate.

On the printing press, the paper passes under each of the four plates. Each plate holds a different color of ink. Without a magnifier, our human eyes cannot see the tiny dots that make up a picture. The colored dots all seem to blend together—just as they would appear if you mixed them from colored paints. But if you look at the picture with a powerful magnifier, you well see these colors break down into the four colors used to print them. ☐

Cyan

Magenta

Black

Yellow

PHOTOGRAPHY BY FERNE SALTZMAN, OFFICIAL BALLOON FIESTA PHOTOGRAPHER, © ALBUQUERQUE INTERNATIONAL BALLOON FIESTA INC.

In modern printing, four plates, each representing a different color—cyan, magenta, yellow, and black—are made. Use a magnifier to look at each picture. You will see they are made from dots of the four different colors. When these colors are combined, they produce a full-color picture.

A Green Engine Driven by the Sun

A giant snake slides silently across the wet floor of the Amazon rainforest. It's a 6-meter long anaconda—the largest snake in world—and it is searching for a meal. Perhaps it will find a juicy capybara, a sort of giant guinea pig. If it's lucky, it may catch an unwary sloth on one of the sloth's rare visits to the forest floor.

The anaconda's method of capture is to squeeze its victim in the giant coils of its body until the victim stops breathing. But all this slithering and crushing requires the snake to use its giant muscles. These muscles—and the snake's other life processes—use energy. The snake gets its energy from food—perhaps today it will be the sloth. Of course, the snake never stops to think where the energy in food comes from. Do you?

Viewed from above, the green rainforest canopy hides the forest floor. Why is the canopy green? What is its function? These answers lie in the way chlorophyll absorbs and reflects sunlight.

Above the hunting anaconda is a canopy of green formed by the giant forest trees. Viewed from above, the forest stretches out in all directions—green as far as the eye can see. Could all this green have something to do with how the snake gets its energy? In fact, this rainforest is an enormous food factory powered by sunlight.

A green chemical in leaves called chlorophyll harnesses the light energy from the Sun. Chlorophyll absorbs some wavelengths of sunlight and reflects others. The forest canopy looks green because its leaves reflect green light. Chlorophyll uses some of the light energy it absorbs to drive chemical

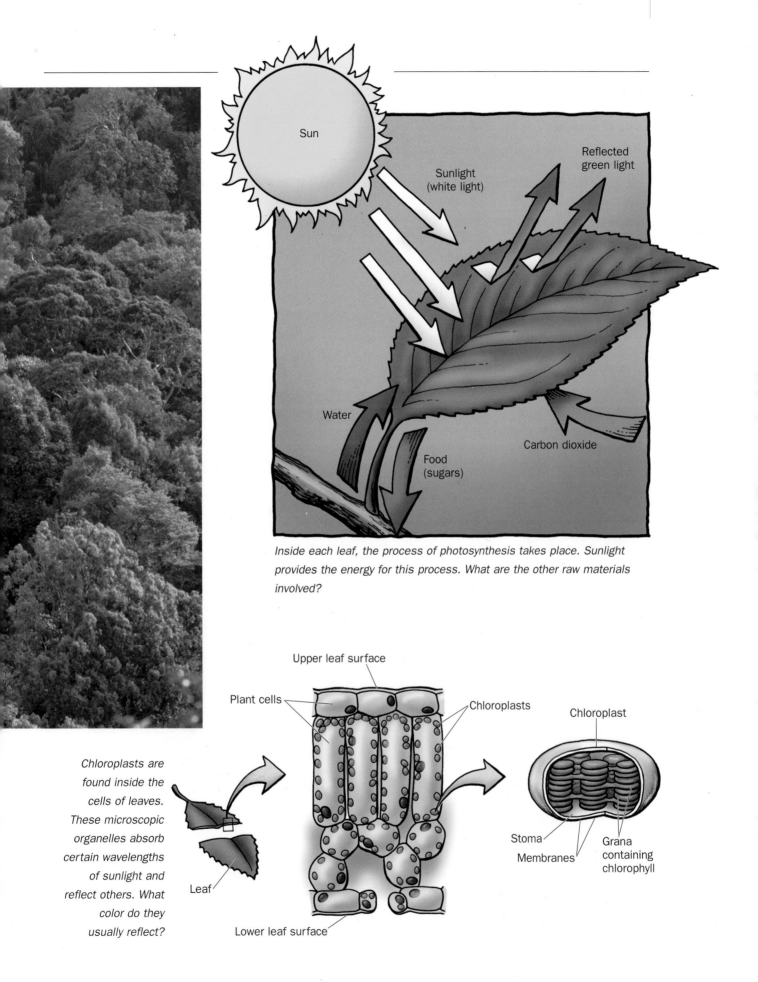

Inside each leaf, the process of photosynthesis takes place. Sunlight provides the energy for this process. What are the other raw materials involved?

Chloroplasts are found inside the cells of leaves. These microscopic organelles absorb certain wavelengths of sunlight and reflect others. What color do they usually reflect?

Sun

Sunlight (white light)

Reflected green light

Water

Food (sugars)

Carbon dioxide

Upper leaf surface

Plant cells

Chloroplasts

Chloroplast

Leaf

Lower leaf surface

Stoma

Membranes

Grana containing chlorophyll

reactions. It transforms light energy into chemical energy—food. This food-making process is called photosynthesis, which means "making with light."

Inside each leaf cell are special tiny structures called chloroplasts containing chlorophyll. The flat leaves and the arrangement of chloroplasts in the cells are adapted to absorb sunlight. But plants need more than just chlorophyll and sunlight to make food by photosynthesis. Giant roots collect water from the shallow forest soil. Leaves absorb carbon dioxide from the air.

Each tree battles its neighbor for the resources needed for photosynthesis. The trees struggle upward competing against each other for light. Their huge roots and trunks support the branches and leaves of the canopy and also act as a highway for water and nutrients needed by the chloroplasts. Inside each chloroplast, the energy from the Sun is used to combine water and carbon dioxide (CO_2) to make sugars and starch. Each tree uses these substances to provide energy for its life processes. It also uses them to make more leaves, branches, flowers, and fruits.

The anaconda is the world's largest species of snake. It uses powerful muscles to squeeze its prey to death. These muscles use energy when they contract. Where does this energy come from?

These leaves and fruits will in turn provide food energy for the sloth and the capybara.

The unsuspecting sloth chews leaves as it carefully descends a tree trunk to the forest floor. The capybara feeds on fruit recently fallen from the trees. The trees of the rainforest canopy provide the sloth with food energy. But this canopy of trees also blocks out the sunlight. In the semi-darkness of the forest floor there is little protection from the anaconda. Nearby, the snake, hunting by its sense of smell, tastes the air with a forked tongue.

Suddenly, the snake seizes the sloth and wraps its long body around it. The snake has found the energy—food—it needs to sustain itself. It doesn't realize that this food energy has come indirectly from the Sun high above the forest canopy, through leaves of the forest to the leaf-eating sloth. The snake never sees the source of its energy. The Sun is hidden by the food factory of the forest canopy. □

© THOMAS CIDA/VISUALS UNLIMITED

This sloth spends most of its life in the trees of the Amazon Rainforest eating leaves. The energy in its food comes from the Sun. Sloths are often slightly green. That's because microscopic plants containing chlorophyll live in their fur.

12
Colored Light

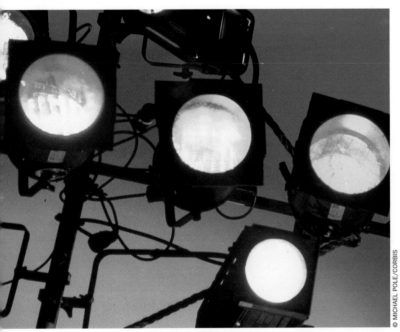

On a visit to a theater you may see lights like these. What is their function and how do they work?

© MICHAEL POLE/CORBIS

INTRODUCTION

Imagine you're at the theater, an opera, or a musical. The lights of the theater darken for the performance. A hush descends over the audience as the curtains slide open. The stage looks dark. Suddenly there is a blaze of color as the star of the performance makes her entrance bathed in colored light. Where is this light coming from? Above, and to either side of the stage, you locate the source of this light. Large numbers of spotlights—some fixed to gantries, a few directed by hand—point at the stage. A few emit white light, but most shine a beam of colored light onto the stage. How is this colored light produced? How are the different colors used to set the scene on the stage combined? What happens when colored lights are mixed? How do these colors affect the appearance of the props and costumes? In Lesson 11, you determined that colored objects look colored because they absorb—or subtract—some of the colors from the light that falls on them and reflect other colors. Objects appear to be the color of the colors they reflect. What name did we give to this type of color mixing? In this lesson, you will investigate another type of color mixing. This color mixing process takes place when the colors from colored lights are added together. Can you guess the name that is given to this type of color mixing?

OBJECTIVES FOR THIS LESSON

Investigate what happens when lights of different colors are mixed together.

Discuss how this type of color mixing is used.

Getting Started

1. Imagine you are in charge of lighting the stage for a concert or play. You have red, green, and blue spotlights. With your group, predict which colors you could make by combining the colors of the spotlights.

2. Record your predictions in the Predictions section of Table 1 on Student Sheet 12.1: Mixing Colored Lights. Be prepared to share your predictions with the class.

Inquiry 12.1
Mixing Colored Lights

PROCEDURE

1. One member of your group should collect the plastic box of materials.

2. Working with your group, come up with a procedure to use the materials available to test the predictions you made in "Getting Started." Record the materials you use and your procedure in Table 1. Use diagrams where appropriate.

3. Devise a data table in Table 1 for your results.

4. Test your predictions and record your results.

5. In the Conclusions section of Table 1, write a paragraph explaining what you can conclude from your inquiry.

MATERIALS FOR LESSON 12

For you
1 copy of Student Sheet 12.1: Mixing Colored Lights
1 copy of Student Sheet 12.2: Assessment Review—Part 1
1 copy of Student Sheet 12.3: Sample Assessment Questions for Part 1

For your group
3 flashlights
6 D-cell batteries
1 red filter
1 green filter
1 blue filter

REFLECTING ON WHAT YOU'VE DONE

1. The type of mixing you explored in Inquiry 12.1 is called additive color mixing. In additive color mixing, red, green, and blue are the primary colors. Discuss A and B with your group and then record your answers on Student Sheet 12.1.

A. Why is the term "primary colors" used to describe red, green, and blue colors in additive color mixing?

B. Why do you think this type of mixing is called additive color mixing?

2. In Lesson 11, you learned about color mixing that subtracts color—subtractive color mixing.

C. Write a short paragraph that describes how additive color mixing differs from subtractive color mixing.

3. Read "About Color Vision and Color Mixing."

About Color Vision and Color Mixing

When you used a prism or your spectroscope to split white light into its different wavelengths, the colors you observed were different wavelengths of light. Yellow, for example, was a small range of wavelengths that looked yellow.

Because of the way our eyes detect color, we perceive mixtures of colors as one color. For example, you already know that white is a mixture of colors. The yellow you made with your flashlights is another example of this. It was not one wavelength of light. It was made from a mixture of two other colors—red and green—that your eyes detected and your brain perceived as being yellow. So the brain perceives yellow in two ways: pure yellow wavelengths or mixtures of red and green wavelengths.

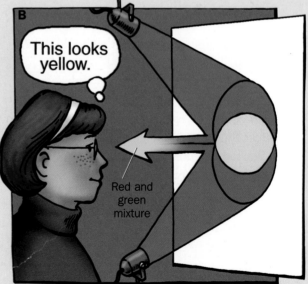

A. The yellow from a rainbow, prism, or spectroscope is a pure color consisting of "yellow wavelengths."

B. This yellow is produced differently. It comes from the yellow we see when red and green lights are mixed. No wavelengths corresponding to yellow light are reaching the eye.

Red, Green, and Blue Entertainment

Although the visible spectrum contains a continuous range of colors from red to violet, our eyes can be tricked into seeing all these colors by mixing only three of them: red, green, and blue. In fact, we allow TV to use this trick every time we watch it.

Turn on a color TV. Look closely at the screen. If you have a magnifying glass, use it to study the picture on the screen. What do you see? If you look very closely at the screen, you will find the picture the TV produces on the screen is made up of thousands of dots. Each dot is a red, green, or blue light. Where do these dots come from? How do they light up? How do they make a moving color picture?

Here's how it works. The inside of the front of your TV screen is made up of thousands of dots, or pixels, arranged in groups of three.

Imagine watching a TV like this one. The picture was only in black and white. Why do you think it was easier and cheaper to make a black-and-white TV?

NATIONAL LIBRARY OF MEDICINE, NATIONAL INSTITUTES OF HEALTH

Each group contains one red, one green, and one blue pixel. Three beams of electrons (one for making each color) race across the screen targeting certain pixels through thousands of tiny holes positioned just behind the screen (in what is called the shadow mask). If a beam hits a pixel, the pixel glows. The beams use these pixels to draw a different picture about 30 times every second! As these pictures flash on the screen, they appear to our eyes as a moving image.

From Signal to a Video Picture

Where do these pictures come from? A TV receives signals, either as radio wave signals through its antenna or satellite receiver or as signals via cable. It converts the signals to sound (audio) and pictures (video). The video part of the signal is further decoded into signals for red, green, and blue. These signals are used to control the electron beams that light up the appropriate colored pixels on the screen. By lighting different pixels in a group, the beams trick the eye into seeing different colors—through additive color mixing. If the red and green pixels in one group are lit, your eyes see yellow. If the beam lights up all three in the group (red, green, and blue), your eyes see white. (This is the same type of color mixing you observed when you shined the flashlights through the colored filters.) By changing the combination and brightness of each of colored pixels, the TV can create thousands of colors. □

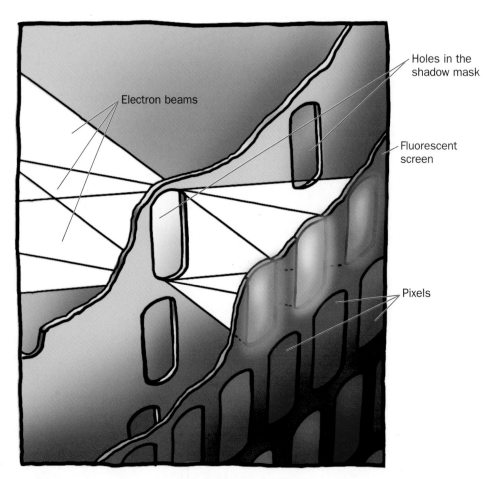

A TV picture is made up of thousands of dots, or pixels. Each pixel is red, green, or blue. They are so small that you can not see them individually, so they are able to appear as a solid color picture.

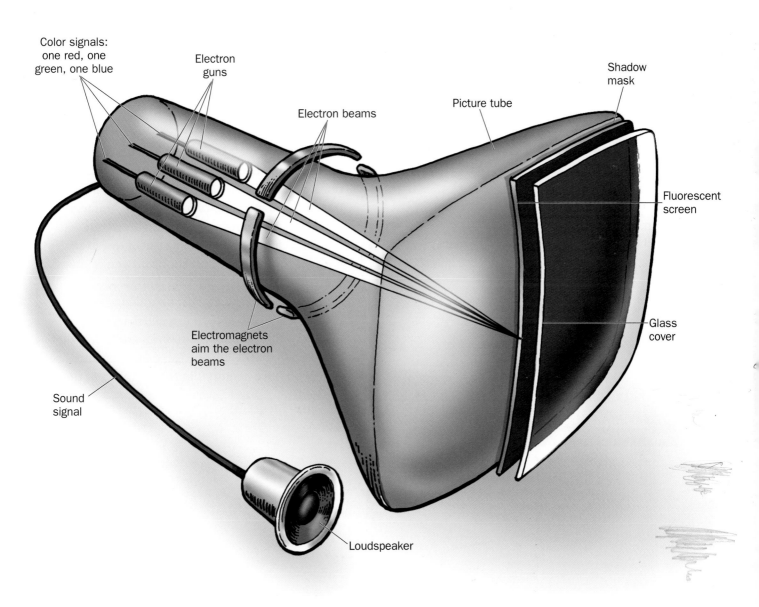

Color signals:
one red, one
green, one blue

Electron
guns

Electron beams

Picture tube

Shadow
mask

Fluorescent
screen

Glass
cover

Electromagnets
aim the electron
beams

Sound
signal

Loudspeaker

Inside a TV set, there are three electron guns, one for each color. These guns fire beams of electrons that make the red, green, or blue pixels glow to form a picture of many colors by using additive color mixing. The guns scan alternate lines of pixels that make up each picture. Each picture is therefore scanned onto the screen twice—60 scans or 30 complete pictures each second.

13

Part 1 Assessment—How Far Have We Come?

Scientific investigations often involve careful measurement and recording of data.

INTRODUCTION

This lesson is the assessment for Part 1: The Nature of Light. The assessment is in two sections. In Section A, you will conduct an inquiry into the size of shadows on a screen. You will take measurements and collect, record, and interpret data. Section B consists of questions, both multiple-choice and short-answer. Some of these require you to use your knowledge and skills to interpret diagrams, data tables, and experiments. You and your teacher will use the results of this assessment to evaluate how well you can apply the knowledge, concepts, and skills you have acquired in the first part of the module.

OBJECTIVES FOR THIS LESSON

Conduct an inquiry into the size of shadows produced on a screen.

Record and interpret data.

Use knowledge and skills acquired to answer questions that relate to Part 1: The Nature of Light.

Getting Started

1. Your teacher will tell you when to do each section of the assessment and how long you will have for each section.

2. In both sections, your work will be assessed partly on your layout, labeling, and drawing of data tables and diagrams.

MATERIALS FOR LESSON 13

For you

- 1 copy of Student Sheet 13.1: Section A—Performance Assessment
- 1 copy of Student Sheet 13.2: Section B—Written Assessment Question Sheet
- 1 copy of Student Sheet 13.3: Section B—Written Assessment Answer Sheet

(Your teacher will explain whether the materials listed below are for you, or for you and your lab partner)

- 1 assembled light stand
- 1 white screen
- 2 plastic stands
- 1 black paper square attached to a craft stick
- 1 meterstick
- 1 metric ruler
- 1 sheet of white paper
- 2 binder clips

SAFETY TIP

Do not touch the lightbulb in the light stand. It gets very hot and may cause painful burns.

SECTION A—PERFORMANCE ASSESSMENT

Inquiry 13.1
Measuring Shadows

PROCEDURE

Read all instructions before you start working.

1. Set up the light stand so that the light-bulb filament is horizontal.

2. Place the screen 50 cm from the end of the lightbulb filament.

3. Use the binder clips to attach the white paper to the white screen.

4. Use the black square (attached to the stick) to produce a shadow on the paper on the screen (see Figure 13.1).

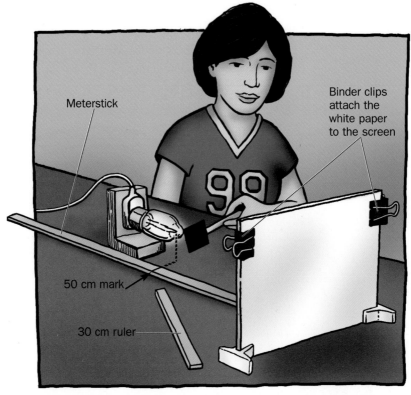

Meterstick

Binder clips attach the white paper to the screen

50 cm mark

30 cm ruler

Figure 13.1 *Use this apparatus to find the area of the shadow you produce on the paper.*

5. Measure the size of your shadow (in cm) when the black square is 5 cm from the screen.

A. Record the dimensions of the shadow.

B. Calculate the area of the shadow (width × height) in square centimeters.

6. Repeat this procedure, measuring the size of the shadow at four *additional* distances farther from the screen.

C. Record *all five* sets of measurements of the distance of the black paper square from the screen, shadow dimensions, and shadow area in a data table of your own design.

D. What can you conclude from your observations?

E. Use *words and a labeled diagram(s)* to explain your observations.

SECTION B —WRITTEN ASSESSMENT

Your teacher will outline the procedure for taking Section B of the assessment.

PART 2 Reflection and Refraction

14
Introducing Mirrors

Why are the letters on the front of this ambulance written like this?

© AUDREY GILSON/VISUALS UNLIMITED

INTRODUCTION

Objects can be seen because they either emit or reflect light. You have investigated how objects reflect some colors and absorb others. Apart from color, do all objects reflect light in the same way? Think about this question the next time you are in a parking lot. Compare the surface of a recently washed and waxed car with the surface of one that is dirty. Here is a clue: What can you see in one but not in the other?

OBJECTIVES FOR THIS LESSON

Observe and discuss different types of reflection.

Investigate what you see in a flat (plane) mirror.

Make predictions about what you will see in a plane mirror.

Describe the features of an image formed in a plane mirror.

Getting Started

1. One member of your group should collect the plastic box of materials. Divide the materials between the pairs in your group.

2. Examine the white screen, mirror, and piece of half-silvered glass. Compare what they do to light that falls on them. Discuss your observations and ideas with your partner. Be prepared to share your observations with the class.

MATERIALS FOR LESSON 14

For you

1 copy of Student Sheet 14.2: Where Is the Image in the Mirror?

1 copy of Student Sheet 14.3: Predicting and Recognizing Mirror Images

For you and your lab partner

1 large mirror

1 white screen

1 piece of half-silvered glass

2 plastic stands

2 wooden blocks

1 metric ruler, 30 cm (12″)

1 adhesive dot

© DAVID MARSLAND

A very smooth surface reflects light in such a way that an image is formed. Light from this town produces a reflection in the almost-smooth river that flows past it. The river is acting as a mirror. Would the reflection be visible if the water surface was very rough?

REFLECTING LIGHT

All surfaces, except those surfaces that are completely black, reflect light. How light behaves when it reflects off a surface depends on the smoothness of the surface. Rough surfaces reflect light, but you cannot see an image (a reflection) in rough surfaces. Clear images or reflections—like those seen in mirrors—can only be seen in very smooth surfaces that reflect light.

Rough surfaces can be designed to reflect large amounts of light. Both safety clothing and road signs are designed to reflect lots of light from car headlights, making the wearer or the sign more visible at night.

3M™ SCOTCHLITE™ REFLECTIVE MATERIAL 3M AND SCOTCHLITE ARE TRADEMARKS OF 3M COMPANY

Be safe at night. Wear reflective clothing.

How does your mirror image look and behave compared with your face?

Inquiry 14.1
Looking at Reflections

PROCEDURE

1. *Without looking in a mirror* describe to your partner how a mirror image (perhaps a mirror image of your face) differs from the object it reflects.

A. In your science notebook, record your description *before* proceeding to the next step.

2. Look at your face in the mirror. Try the following. (Here's a clue: Try not to think of the reflection as another person looking back at you—just record what you observe.)

A. Touch your left ear with your left hand.

On which side of the mirror is your left hand?

B. Touch your right ear with your right hand.

On which side of the mirror is your right hand?

C. Place your fingertip on the right-hand side of the mirror.

On which side of the mirror is the reflection of your finger?

Which way is your finger pointing?

3. Based on your observations, which of the following statements is correct?

A mirror image is reversed left to right.

A mirror image is reversed front to back (that is, the front of the image is facing back toward you).

Inquiry 14.2
Where Is the Image in the Mirror?

PROCEDURE

1. Spend a few minutes investigating what determines the size and position of your image in a plane (that is, flat) mirror. Discuss your observations and ideas with your partner.

2. Set up one of the wooden blocks and the half-silvered glass, as shown in Figure 14.1. The silvered side of the glass should face the observer.

3. Position your head as shown in Figure 14.1, so that you are looking at the block and toward the half-silvered glass with only one eye open. Record your responses to A–H on Student Sheet 14.2: Where Is the Image in the Mirror?

A. Describe what you observe when you look at the half-silvered glass.

4. Keep your head in this position and have your partner place the second block behind the glass. Guide your partner to move the second block around until it exactly matches the *image* of the first block in the half-silvered glass (see Figure 14.2).

B. How many positions of the second block (behind the half-silvered glass) exactly match the position of the image of the first block (the object in front of the glass)?

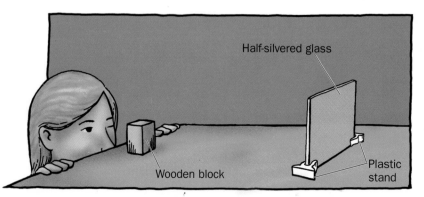

Figure 14.1 *Set up the half-silvered glass as shown. Place one of the blocks about 30 cm in front of the glass.*

SAFETY TIP

Have your partner separate the clips of each plastic stand, while you carefully insert the sides of the half-silvered glass.

Figure 14.2 *With only one eye open, guide your partner to move the second block around until it exactly matches the image of the first block (the object).*

5. Measure the distance of both blocks from the silvered surface of the half-silvered glass.

C. Record your measurements.

6. Repeat this procedure with the first block positioned at different distances from the front of the half-silvered glass. (Decide how many measurements you should make.)

D. Design a data table and record all your measurements.

7. Compare your results with those of another pair of students.

E. From the data you have collected, what can you conclude about the position of an image in the half-silvered glass?

F. Do you think what you have observed with the block and half-silvered glass applies to the image formed by a plane mirror? Suggest how you could test your answer.

8. Look at the plane mirror. Discuss the following question with your partner, then record your answer:

G. When you look at an image in a plane mirror, does the image appear to be on or in the mirror's surface, behind the mirror, or in front of the mirror?

9. Use the instructions in this step and Steps 10–12 to test your ideas.

• Hold your hand at arm's length while you are facing a distant object.
• Focus your eyes on your hand.

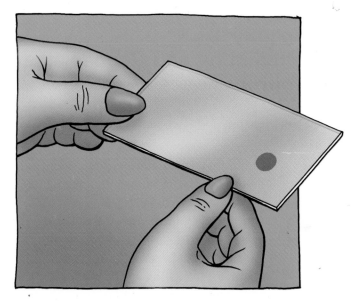

Figure 14.3 *Place an adhesive dot on the surface of the mirror about 3 cm in from the bottom right corner.*

• Now focus your eyes on the distant object.

Can you focus on both your hand and the distant object at the same time?

10. Place an adhesive dot on the surface of the mirror about 3 cm in from the bottom right corner (see Figure 14.3).

11. Look at the image of your face in the mirror.

Can you focus on the dot and the image of your face at the same time?

12. Compare the observations you made about your hand and a distant object (in Step 9) with your observations of the image of your face in the mirror and the dot on the mirror.

H. Where do you think the *image* of your face is in relation to the surface of the mirror?

Inquiry 14.3
Predicting and Recognizing Mirror Images

PROCEDURE

1. In the previous inquiries, you discovered that the *image* produced in a plane mirror or piece of half-silvered glass is different from the *object* reflected in the mirror or half-silvered glass. Can you use this information to predict the appearance of a mirror image? Record your responses to A–C on Student Sheet 14.3: Predicting and Recognizing Mirror Images.

A. Look at the image of symbols within the set of squares shown in Figure 14.4. On the identical set of squares *on the student sheet,* draw the image—*without using a mirror*—as it would appear in a plane mirror placed along the line XY.

2. When you have completed your drawing, test it by placing the mirror on the line XY. Compare the image you drew with the one produced in the mirror. If you have made errors, figure out why you made them and then make corrections.

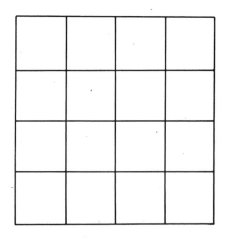

X _ _ _ _ _ _ _ _ _ _ _ _ _ Y

Place mirror on this line to check your predictions

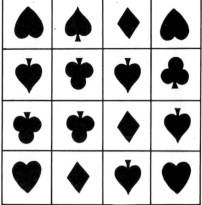

Figure 14.4 *On Student Sheet 14.3, draw the image—without using a mirror—as it would appear in a plane mirror placed along the line XY.*

Figure 14.5 *Try writing your name while looking in the mirror. Why is it so difficult?*

3. Stand your mirror up along the line under B on the student sheet. Look in the mirror.

B. Try writing your name while looking in the mirror, as shown in Figure 14.5. Don't peek at the paper. Keep looking in the mirror; your teacher is watching you!

4. Recognizing mirror images can be difficult. Look at the two sets of photographs in Figure 14.6.

C. Which of these photographs are mirror images of each other—Set 1 or Set 2?

5. Use a mirror to check your answer to C.

REFLECTING ON WHAT YOU'VE DONE
Spend a few minutes discussing with your group what you have discovered about plane mirrors and the images formed in them.

A. Write a paragraph on Student Sheet 14.3 summarizing your findings. Be prepared to share your paragraph with the class.

Figure 14.6 *Which of these two sets of photographs are mirror images of one another? How can you tell they are mirror images? Use a mirror to check your answer.*

MIRROR MAKERS

Flat glass mirrors became popular in the 16th and 17th centuries. This drawing shows these mirrors being made by hand. The process was quite dangerous because it often involved the use of the poisonous metal mercury.

Imagine one of your prehistoric ancestors gazing at his or her face in a still pool. Without an understanding of the nature of light, this reflected image must have seemed magical. Perhaps this is why you often find mirrors in legends, fairy tales, and stories.

For most of human history, a still water surface may have been the only mirror available. The first manufactured mirrors were made probably from polished volcanic glass—the rock obsidian. Examples of these stone-age mirrors have been found in central Turkey. Like all mirror surfaces, these rock mirrors had to be very smooth. Bumps on a mirror's surface must be less than the wavelength of light being reflected. For visible light, this means bumps can be no bigger than 0.00005 centimeters (5.0×10^{-5} cm). Surfaces with bumps bigger than this reflect light, but you cannot see images in them. The volcanic glass mirrors found in Turkey were buried with their owners in graves more than eight thousand years old. Mirrors were valuable items, worth taking into a legendary afterlife.

These hand mirrors were made sometime between 1539 B.C. and 1292 B.C. in Egypt. Hand mirrors like these made from polished metal were valuable possessions.

Once people learned how to use metal, they polished it to make mirrors. Early metal mirrors were made from copper, bronze, and silver and often were elaborately decorated.

The Romans used metal mirrors. They also tried making mirrors from glass. They put thin layers of gold, copper, or silver onto the back of curved pieces of glass. Flat glass mirrors were not made in large numbers until the 16th century. The glassmakers of Venice perfected the technique for making flat mirrors. They backed these mirrors with a mixture of the metals tin and mercury. In the mid-1800s, this process of mixing tin and mercury—which is very poisonous—was replaced by a chemical process that backed mirrors with silver.

Today most mirrors are still made from glass backed with metal. Usually silver or aluminum is sprayed—or evaporated and condensed—onto the back of the glass. □

BINSWANGER MIRROR

In modern mirror-making, a shiny reflective surface is sprayed onto flat glass.

Mirrors in Myth

Mirrors and reflections play a big part in some stories, legends, and fairy tales. But when you understand how reflections are formed, mirrors become less mysterious. Do you know any stories in which mirrors play an important role?

PLATE WITH BORDER OF GROTESQUES ON AN ORANGE GROUND; IN THE CENTER, NARCISSUS GAZING AT HIS REFLECTION IN A FOUNTAIN, WIDENER COLLECTION, PHOTOGRAPH © 2002 BOARD OF TRUSTEES, NATIONAL GALLERY OF ART, WASHINGTON.

In Greek myth, Narcissus was so beautiful that he fell in love with his own reflection. His love affair with himself led to his untimely death by drowning.

ILLUSTRATION BY JOHN TENNIEL

A mirror was the door to a magic world in Lewis Carroll's Through the Looking Glass.

15

How Is Light Reflected?

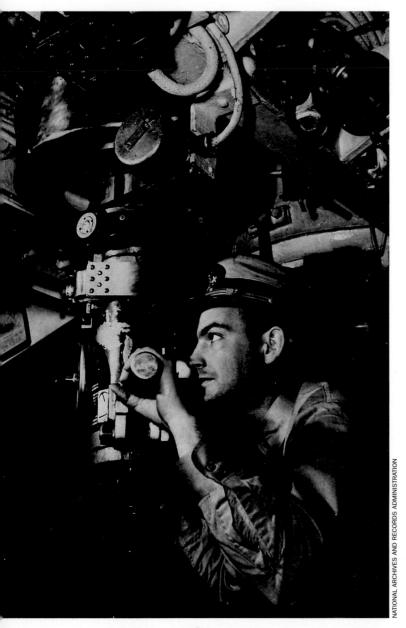

What is this naval officer looking through?
What is it used for? How does it work?

NATIONAL ARCHIVES AND RECORDS ADMINISTRATION

INTRODUCTION

In Lesson 14, you observed some of the characteristics of images produced by a plane mirror. You discovered that the images appeared to be behind the mirror. Is it possible to use your knowledge of the behavior of light to explain how these images are produced? In this lesson, you will conduct an inquiry on what happens to light when it is reflected from a plane mirror. You then will apply what you have discovered to help you to predict and control the direction of a ray of light. You also will apply what you have discovered to build an optical device called a periscope.

OBJECTIVES FOR THIS LESSON

Observe and measure reflection of light rays off a plane mirror.

Use mirrors to redirect light rays.

Build an optical device that uses mirrors.

Discuss the formation of an image in a plane mirror.

Getting Started

1. Have one member of your group collect the plastic box of materials. You will be recording all your responses for this lesson in your science notebook.

2. Work with your group to set up the ray box so that it produces a single ray of light as shown in Figure 15.1.

3. Experiment with placing the large mirror into the path of the ray of light. Record your observations.

MATERIALS FOR LESSON 15

For your group
- 1 ray box
- 1 ray box lid
- 1 60-W clear halogen lightbulb
- 1 extension cord
- 1 bulb holder
- 1 narrow-slit ray box mask
- 1 wide-slit ray box mask
- 2 no-slit ray box masks
- 1 white screen
- 1 comb
- 1 large mirror
- 1 sheet of white paper
- 1 box of colored pencils
- 1 protractor
- 4 plastic stands
- 1 copy of Inquiry Master 15.1: Protractor Paper for Inquiry 15.1

For you and your lab partner
- 1 cardboard tube
- 2 small mirrors
- 1 metric ruler, 30 cm (12")
- 1 protractor
- 1 pair of scissors
  Masking tape

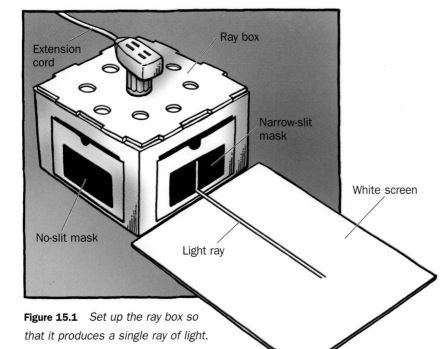

Figure 15.1 *Set up the ray box so that it produces a single ray of light.*

Labels: Extension cord, Ray box, Narrow-slit mask, White screen, No-slit mask, Light ray

> **SAFETY TIP**
>
> Do not touch the lightbulb. It gets hot and may burn your fingers.

Inquiry 15.1
Measuring
Reflection

PROCEDURE

1. Have one member of your group use the scissors to cut along the cutout lines on the protractor paper.

2. Working with your group, set up the apparatus as shown in Figure 15.2. The base of the large mirror should lie along the baseline of the protractor paper. Position the mirror so that its center approximately matches the center of the baseline. Throughout this inquiry, the mirror should stay in this position on the protractor paper. (If you prefer, you may tape your protractor paper to your mirror in the correct position.)

3. Move the mirror and protractor paper so that the ray of light from the narrow slit passes down the 60° line of the protractor paper. The ray should strike the mirror where the 0° line (the line perpendicular to the mirror, which is called the normal) meets at the center of the baseline, as shown in Figure 15.3.

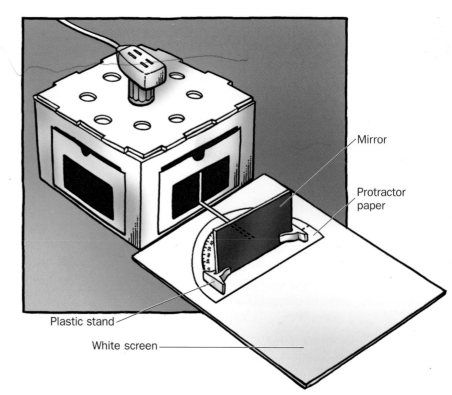

Figure 15.2 *Position the large mirror, white screen, and protractor paper as shown.*

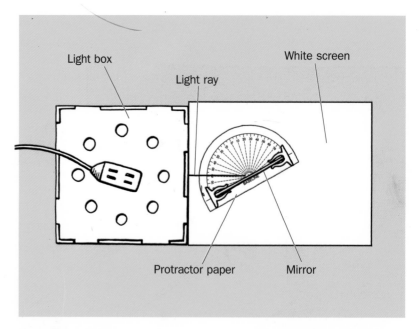

Figure 15.3 *Move the mirror and protractor paper so that the ray of light from the narrow slit passes down the 60° line of the protractor paper. The ray should strike the mirror where the 0° line (the line perpendicular to the mirror, which is called the normal) meets at the center of the baseline.*

4. On the protractor paper, use a colored pencil and a ruler to accurately draw a line that follows the ray of light from the center of the ray box to the large mirror. This ray is called the *incident ray*. Next draw a line that follows the center of the ray of light reflected from the mirror. This ray is called the *reflected ray*.

5. Move the mirror and protractor paper to change the angle of the incident ray. Aim the ray at the same point on the mirror. Draw a line on the protractor paper (in a different color) that follows the incident ray and another line that follows the reflected ray. Do not confuse this set of rays with the rays you recorded in Step 4.

6. Repeat Step 5 a few more times.

7. For each set of incident and reflected rays, use the protractor paper to determine the angle between each ray and the line perpendicular to the mirror (the line labeled "Normal" in Figure 15.4).

8. Design and then draw a table for your data in your notebook. Record your data.

9. Compare your results with those from another group. What can you conclude from your results? Record your ideas.

10. Move the white screen and the mirror to the side of the ray box with the wide-slit mask. Use the comb against the wide-slit mask to produce multiple rays as shown in Figure 15.5. Direct the rays at the mirror. Draw what you observe. Be prepared to share your observations with the class.

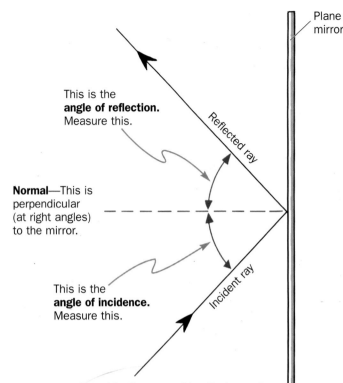

Figure 15.4 *Use this diagram to identify the angle of incidence and angle of reflection for each ray. Use the protractor paper to measure these angles.*

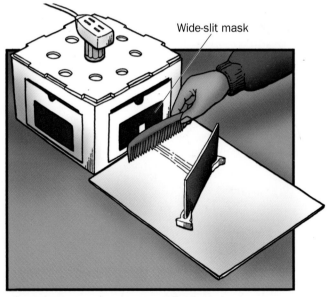

Figure 15.5 *Direct multiple rays at the mirror. What do you observe?*

Inquiry 15.2
Changing the Path of a Light Ray

PROCEDURE

1. Look at the ray box setup from Inquiry 15.1. Predict the angle at which the mirror will have to be held so that the ray of light turns through a right angle (90°). Record your prediction and write a sentence explaining how you reached it.

2. Test your prediction. Use the protractor to measure the angles.

3. Keep your apparatus in place, and use a second mirror to redirect the light ray so that it continues on each of the following paths:

- a path that is parallel to the existing ray leaving the box and in the same direction
- a path that is parallel to the existing ray leaving the box, but in the opposite direction
- a path that returns the ray to the slit in the ray box

4. Which group in the class can construct the most complicated ray path using multiple mirrors? Use all the mirrors and plastic stands at your disposal. Spend a few minutes constructing your ray path. *What problem do you encounter? Can you reflect light from the same ray off the same mirror more than once? Compare your ray path with those constructed by other groups.*

5. Read "Redirecting Light, Images, and the Law of Reflection."

SAFETY TIP

Turn off the ray box immediately after you finish using it. Allow the ray box to cool.

REDIRECTING LIGHT, IMAGES, AND THE LAW OF REFLECTION

You have determined that the angle of reflection from a plane mirror equals the angle of incidence. This rule is called the law of reflection. By altering the angle of a mirror with respect to the incident ray, you can alter the direction in which the ray travels. By reflecting light from one mirror to another, light can be made to change direction many times and can be directed around opaque objects.

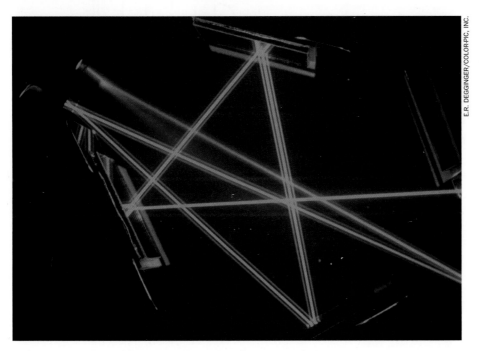

Light can be reflected from one mirrored surface to another.

Inquiry 15.3
Constructing a Device To See Over Objects

PROCEDURE

1. Look at the picture in Figure 15.6. How could you and your partner use the small mirrors, tube, scissors, and tape in the box of materials to construct a device to observe the bird on the feeder? Discuss your ideas with your partner.

2. Your teacher will tell you how to proceed with this inquiry. Be prepared to explain and demonstrate the device you make.

Figure 15.6 *How can she build an optical device that will make it possible to see over the fence?*

REFLECTING ON WHAT YOU'VE DONE

Refer back to your response for Inquiry 1.6 on Student Sheet 1.1. Can you explain now how you were able to use a mirror to look behind you? Redraw your diagram from that inquiry in your notebook. This time add arrows to the rays (to indicate the direction you think the light is traveling) and label the various rays and angles. Write a few sentences using the correct terminology to describe what is happening in your diagram.

EXPLAINING THE VIRTUAL IMAGE

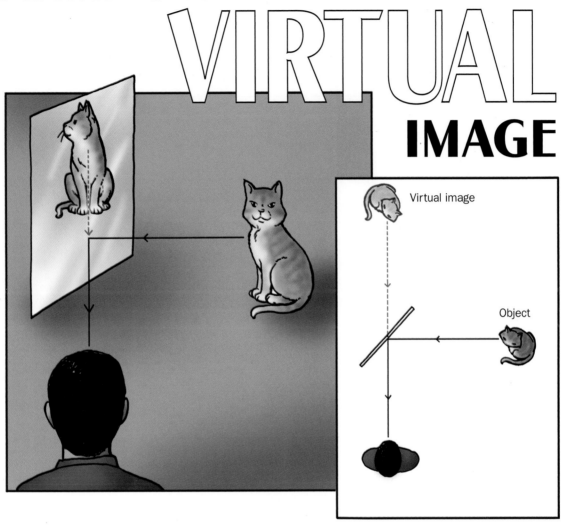

The law of reflection can be used to explain the position of an image seen in a mirror. Imagine looking at an image of an object in a mirror—for example, a cat. You see an image of the cat because some of the light from a source (for example, a lightbulb or the Sun) hits the cat. Because the cat is a rough surface and not a smooth mirror, this light reflects off the cat in many directions. Some of these reflected light rays travel toward the mirror. When these incident rays strike the mirror, they are reflected. Some of these rays are reflected to your eyes. When your eyes detect these rays, you see the image of the cat.

The cat appears to be behind the mirror. This is because your brain assumes that light has traveled in a straight line coming from the image. But your brain does not take into account that the rays of light have been reflected off the mirror. Instead, your brain assumes that the cat lies in a straight line—backward along the direction of the light ray entering your eye. Therefore, you see the cat as being behind the mirror.

The image of the cat also appears to be the same distance behind the mirror as the actual distance the cat sits in front of the mirror. You measured the same phenomenon with the half-silvered glass and wooden blocks in Inquiry 14.2.

The image of the cat formed by a plane mirror is an example of what is called a virtual image. It is called a virtual image—as opposed to a real image—because where it appears to be (behind the mirror) there are no light rays that could be reflected from the object. □

Abu Ali Hasan Ibn al-Haytham

Just like art, literature, and music, science has its roots in many cultures. At the turn of the first millennium—1000 A.D.—the culture and learning of the Greeks, although still important, were ancient history. The Roman Empire's rule over Europe had long before fallen apart and much of Europe was just emerging from the so-called Dark Ages. But other cultures were blossoming.

Islamic influence was expanding and the Islamic world stretched from the borders of India to North Africa and parts of southern Europe.

Many cultures have contributed to current scientific knowledge. Alhazen, or more correctly Abu Ali Hasan Ibn al-Haytham, an Arab from the ancient city of Basra, is one of the founders of the science of optics. He also was one of the earliest developers of the scientific method.

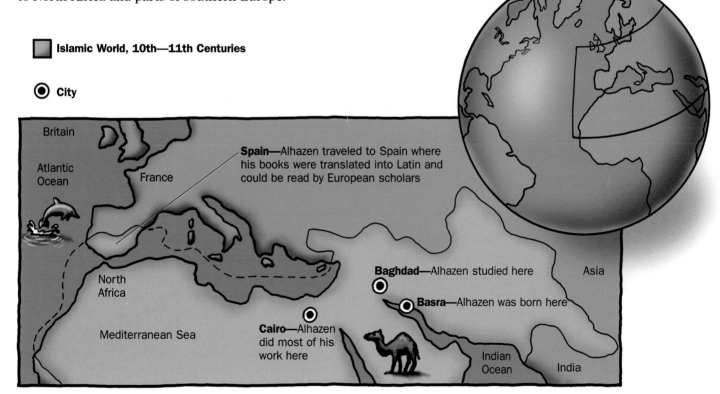

■ **Islamic World, 10th—11th Centuries**

◉ **City**

Britain

Atlantic Ocean

France

Spain—Alhazen traveled to Spain where his books were translated into Latin and could be read by European scholars

North Africa

Mediterranean Sea

Cairo—Alhazen did most of his work here

Baghdad—Alhazen studied here

Basra—Alhazen was born here

Asia

Indian Ocean

India

During Alhazen's lifetime (965–1040), Islamic rule and scholarship stretched from the Indian Ocean to the North Atlantic.

Why can you see sunlight when the Sun is below the horizon and not visible in the sky? Alhazen suggested that light from the Sun below the horizon traveled around Earth by somehow being reflected from high in the atmosphere. We now know this process involves light being scattered from molecules high in the atmosphere. This scattering also bends light around Earth during a lunar eclipse and explains why the Moon often reflects a dim red light during a total eclipse.

Islamic scholars were considered the most learned in the world. They worked in all aspects of art, mathematics, and science and had access to the world's best universities and libraries. They were well educated and widely traveled.

One such scholar was an Arab born in Basra, an important city located in what is now Iraq. His name was Abu Ali Hasan Ibn al-Haytham. He is better known in the Western world by a shortened version of his name, Alhazen. Alhazen was interested in many subjects, but he specialized in mathematics, astronomy, and physics. One of his favorite subjects was optics.

Alhazen liked to design inquiries to test his theories as well as those of others. He studied light from sources such as lamps, fire, the Moon, and the Sun. He suggested that light was a single phenomenon, regardless of its source or color. He conducted experiments to determine that light travels in straight lines. He also studied what happens to light when it enters a transparent material. He used a prism to make a colored spectrum. He even correctly suggested the cause of twilight.

Alhazen investigated how the eyes worked. He was probably the first person to record the

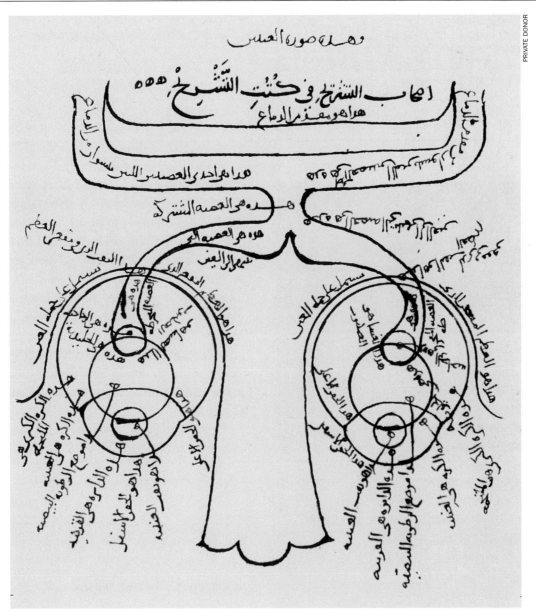

Alhazen investigated how the eyes worked. Here is one of his diagrams of the human visual system.

idea that light travels from an object to the eye, and not in the opposite direction.

Although Alhazen studied human vision, he is best known for his research on reflection. Alhazen's studies of reflection confirmed earlier Greek theories about reflection from plane mirrors—including the law of reflection, which states that the angle of incidence equals the angle of reflection. He then applied these laws to curved mirrors.

Alhazen wrote about 200 books. He developed a scientific methodology, an experimental approach to explaining the natural world. This approach was adopted 500 years later by European scientists in the forefront of a new revolution in the arts and the sciences known as the Renaissance. ☐

16
Bending Mirrors

Curved reflective surfaces, like the one in this astronaut's helmet, produce some strange effects.

NATIONAL AERONAUTICS AND SPACE ADMINISTRATION/PHOTOGRAPH BY CHARLES CONRAD JR.

INTRODUCTION

So far, your investigations of mirrors have involved flat (plane) mirrors. What if you could somehow bend your mirror? Would it reflect light the same way? Would light striking it follow the law of reflection? How would the *way* and *amount* it was bent affect the way it reflects light? What sort of images would curved mirrors produce? In this lesson, you will bend a mirror and investigate how curved mirrors interact with light. As you progress through your investigation, you may find the answers to some of these questions.

OBJECTIVES FOR THIS LESSON

Observe how images seen in normal flat mirrors change as the shape of a mirror is changed from flat to curved.

Describe the images you observe in curved mirrors.

Identify types of curved mirrors.

Investigate how light rays interact with curved mirrors.

Discuss how the law of reflection can be applied to curved mirrors.

Read about and discuss some uses of curved mirrors.

Getting Started

1. One member of your group should collect the plastic box of materials. Each pair should remove a mirror from the box. Take care not to scratch the mirror or get fingerprints on it.

2. Bend the mirror in different ways for a few minutes. This plastic mirror is flexible, but do not bend it too much or it may break.

   What effect does bending the mirror have on the image that appears in the mirror?

3. Experiment with making different images with your mirror. Here are some suggestions:

   • Try making an image of your face that is upside down.
   • Try making an image of your face that is shorter and fatter than normal.
   • Try making an image of your face that is taller and thinner than normal.

4. Think about what you did to the mirror or how you changed your position in relation to the mirror to make these different images. Discuss with the class how you made these and any other interesting images. Then read "Types of Curved Mirrors."

MATERIALS FOR LESSON 16

For you and your lab partner
1 flexible plastic mirror
1 wide-slit ray box mask
1 no-slit ray box mask
1 white screen
1 comb

For your group
1 ray box
1 ray box lid
1 60-W clear halogen lightbulb
1 extension cord
1 bulb holder

Inquiry 16.1
Looking at Convex Mirrors

PROCEDURE

1. Use your flexible mirror to make a convex mirror by bending the top and the bottom of the mirror away from you. Record your observations and responses for this lesson in your science notebook.

A. Describe how the appearance of your reflection changes as you slowly bend the mirror.

2. Hold the mirror in this shape and move it backward and forward in front of your face.

B. Does the image change in any way?

Why is the following statement often written on rearview mirrors: "Objects in the mirror are closer than they appear"? What type of mirrors are they?

Types of Curved Mirrors

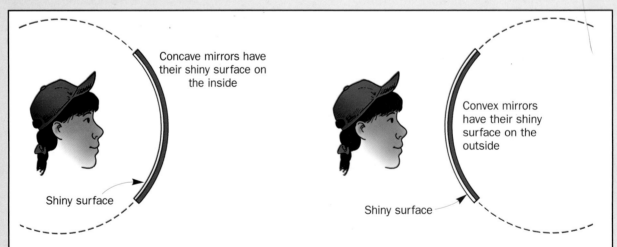

Concave mirrors have their shiny surface on the inside

Shiny surface

Convex mirrors have their shiny surface on the outside

Shiny surface

There are two main types of curved mirrors. Concave mirrors have a shiny surface that bends toward you—like the inside of a shiny sphere. Convex mirrors have a shiny surface that bends away from you—like the outside of a shiny sphere. Can you remember where else in this module you have seen convex and concave mirrors?

3. Set up the ray box and white screen so that each pair in your group can work at opposite ends of the ray box. Attach the wide-slit ray box mask to the end where you are working and place the comb in front of the wide slit as shown in Figure 16.1. (Make sure that the comb is placed in front of the wide slit so that it produces multiple rays.)

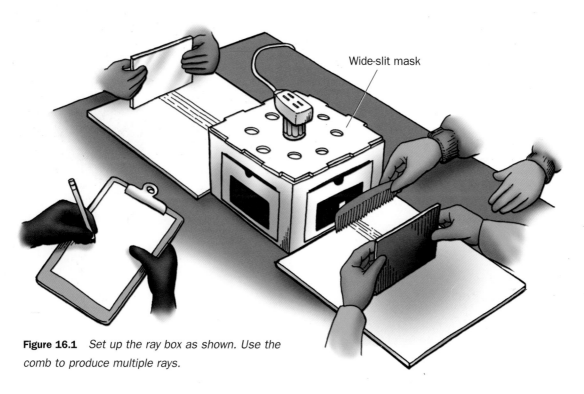

Wide-slit mask

Figure 16.1 *Set up the ray box as shown. Use the comb to produce multiple rays.*

4. Place the mirror in position and then slowly bend its sides away from the comb so that it forms a convex mirror. Make sure the multiple rays fall on the mirror.

C. What do you observe as you bend the mirror?

D. Draw a diagram to show what happens when rays from the ray box strike a convex mirror.

EXPLAINING REFLECTION FROM A CONVEX MIRROR

To understand what happens to light when it strikes a convex mirror, it is useful to think of a convex mirror as being a series of tiny plane mirrors connected together, as shown in the top diagram below.

As a ray strikes one of these tiny mirrors, it is reflected. Its angle of incidence equals the angle of reflection. However, because each mirror is tilted differently, the reflected rays go off in different directions. The reflected rays spread out—that is, they diverge.

Where is the image formed in a convex mirror? Use the photograph below and the diagram (bottom left) to decide whether the image is in front of or behind the mirror. How does the image shown in the photographed mirror compare with the object itself? Is it right-side up (upright) or upside down (inverted)? Is it bigger or smaller than the object?

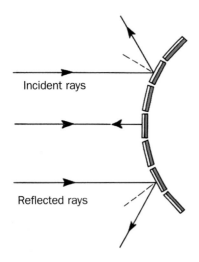

Think of a convex mirror as being made up of many tiny plane mirrors. Each ray that strikes one of these mirrors follows the same law of reflection you studied in Lesson 15.

Is the image in this convex mirror inverted or upright? Bigger or smaller than the object?

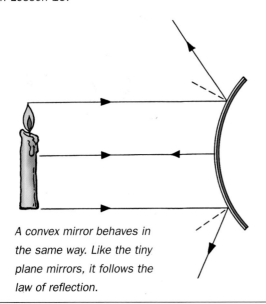

A convex mirror behaves in the same way. Like the tiny plane mirrors, it follows the law of reflection.

Inquiry 16.2
Looking at Concave Mirrors

PROCEDURE

1. Using the materials provided, design a procedure with your partner to investigate reflection from a concave mirror.

   A. Describe your procedure, using diagrams and words.

   B. Record your results and observations. Use diagrams where appropriate.

   C. Write a paragraph that explains how light is reflected from a concave mirror.

2. Discuss how you can use your observations to help you to explain the image(s) you obtained using a concave mirror.

   D. Use words and/or diagrams to record your explanation for the images you obtain.

3. Read "Explaining Reflection From a Concave Mirror."

SAFETY TIP

Turn off the ray box immediately after you finish using it. Allow the ray box to cool.

EXPLAINING REFLECTION FROM A CONCAVE MIRROR

As you have observed, light rays striking the surface of a concave mirror are reflected inward. They are said to converge. Reflection from the surface of a concave mirror, like that from a convex mirror, can be explained by thinking of the surface of the concave mirror as a series of tiny plane mirrors. The angle of incidence equals the angle of reflection of rays for each of these imaginary plane mirrors.

Rays reflected from a concave mirror cross over one another. The point where they cross over is called the focal point of the mirror. This is called the focal point because parallel rays striking the mirror meet at this point—that is, they are focused at that point. The distance from the focal point to the reflective surface of the mirror is called the focal length of the mirror.

What you see in a mirror depends on your position in relation to the focal point. Look at the diagram below. What would be the orientation of the image of the candle—which way would be up—if you were looking at the mirror from point A? What would be the orientation of the image of the candle if you were looking at the mirror from point B?

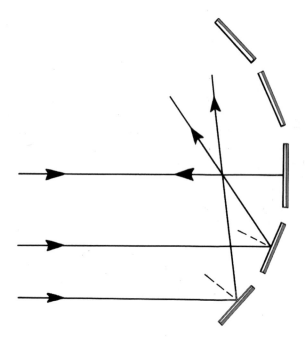

Reflection from a concave mirror can also be thought of as reflection from a series of tiny plane mirrors. With concave mirrors, as in all forms of reflection, the angle of the incident ray is equal to the angle of the reflected ray.

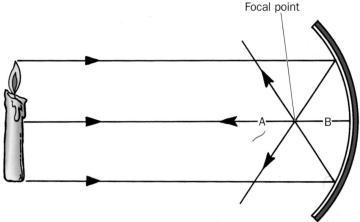

Predict the orientation of the image of the candle if you were looking at it from point A and then from point B.

The images you observe in a concave mirror depend on the distance of the object from the mirror. Some of these images are upright and others are inverted. Can you guess the point at which the images turn over? Makeup and shaving mirrors are concave mirrors. When you stand close to these mirrors, they provide a magnified image of your face—that is, the image of your face is bigger than it would be in a plane mirror in the same position.

Makeup mirrors are concave. When your face is close to the mirror, it appears magnified and upright. The image of your face is a virtual image.

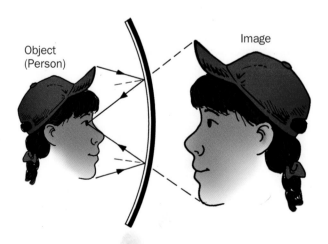

Object (Person)

Image

When an object is within the focal length of a concave mirror, its image is magnified, upright, and virtual. Why is it a virtual image?

REFLECTING ON WHAT YOU'VE DONE

1. Discuss with your group what you have discovered about curved mirrors. Make notes during the discussion.

A. Write a paragraph summarizing what you have learned about curved mirrors.

2. Look at the photograph of a fairground mirror. Where is the surface of the mirror convex? Where is the surface of the mirror concave? Share your ideas with the class.

3. Read "Search and Reflect." Be prepared to explain how mirrors are used as reflectors.

Mirrors can have concave and convex surfaces, like this "trick" fairground mirror. Looking at the image, can you tell where the surface of the mirror is concave and where the surface is convex?

Search and Reflect

Reflectors at War

The year is 1940. It's a quiet, very dark night in the city of London, England. Hardly a light can be seen. Thick curtains cover every window. No street lamps are on. Even the few cars on the street have their headlights partly covered. The city is blacked out— because here, light can bring a rain of death. Suddenly, a wail of sirens and the pounding of distant guns shatter the peace. The city of London has become a battlefield. Nazi planes drop their deadly bombs on the city. Another night of the London Blitz has begun.

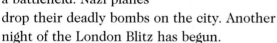
How were the lives of the German World War II pilots put at risk by concave mirrors?

Light is both friend and foe in this battle. The city tries to hide under its cloak of darkness from the searching eyes of enemy bombers. But some of the heavy, slow German planes, loaded with tons of bombs, find their targets anyway. The city lights up first with the flames of burning buildings, which act as beacons for the German pilots. Then beams of light penetrate upward through the smoke and into the night sky. From the ground, these giant searchlights scan the skies for enemy planes. A searchlight beam picks out one bomber. Before it can drop its deadly cargo of bombs onto the densely populated city, the enemy plane is exposed to merciless gunfire from below.

Searchlights were an important weapon in World War II. Their powerful lamps were focused into a beam of light that could penetrate miles up into the sky. Like a giant flashlight, a concave mirror placed behind the lamp focused the beam.

Why was there a concave mirror in this searchlight?

Reflectors Everywhere

Concave reflectors also play an important role in peacetime. Any light designed to provide intense lighting on a limited area contains concave reflectors. By placing the light source (perhaps a lightbulb, a kerosene or gas lamp, or a candle) at the focal point of the concave mirror, light that would have traveled in the opposite direction is reflected forward, making a powerful, highly directional beam of light.

Reflectors are the most common use of concave mirrors. Look at the following pictures of reflectors. Can you think of other places they are used? ☐

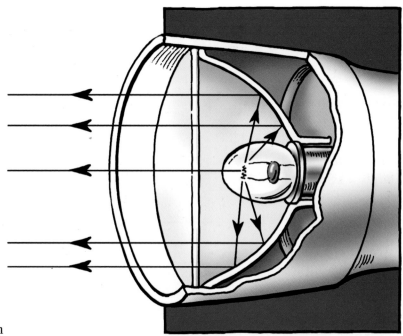

Both flashlights and searchlights contain reflectors. These are concave mirrors that focus the light into a beam.

Searchlights such as these were used to detect night-flying enemy aircraft.

Sometimes the reflector is included inside a lightbulb.

Reflectors are used in headlights of trains, cars, and planes.

Sometimes the reflector takes the form of a reflective lamp shade.

Some types of electromagnetic radiation don't require shiny mirrors. These giant reflectors collect radio waves from distant stars and galaxies. The reflector focuses the waves onto a receiver at the focal point of the reflector. This reversed use of reflection increases the telescope's sensitivity to faint radio signals.

The Trouble With Hubble

FIRST LIGHT: MAY 20, 1990

Astronomers around the world held their breath as a drama unfolded 600 kilometers above Earth. The Hubble Space Telescope was about to start working. Scientists had dreamed for decades of being able to see the universe without having to peer through Earth's atmosphere. Now the telescope moved to capture light that left a distant star cluster 1300 years ago. The $1.5 billion telescope was about to get its first test. Astronomers call this test "first light."

As the telescope opened its "eye," a new tool became available to astronomers. They had high hopes. Would Hubble help them unravel many secrets of the universe?

Does Hubble Need Glasses?
With a huge project such as Hubble, nobody expected everything to be perfect. Its designers expected it to go through a shakedown period during which scientists could solve minor problems. And there were problems. For example, the solar panels, which supply the telescope with electricity from sunlight, were

The Hubble Space Telescope is about the size of a school bus. It orbits Earth at about 27,000 kilometers per hour. It produces very clear images of distant objects because light entering the telescope does not have to pass through Earth's atmosphere. (The air of the atmosphere distorts images viewed by ground-based telescopes.)

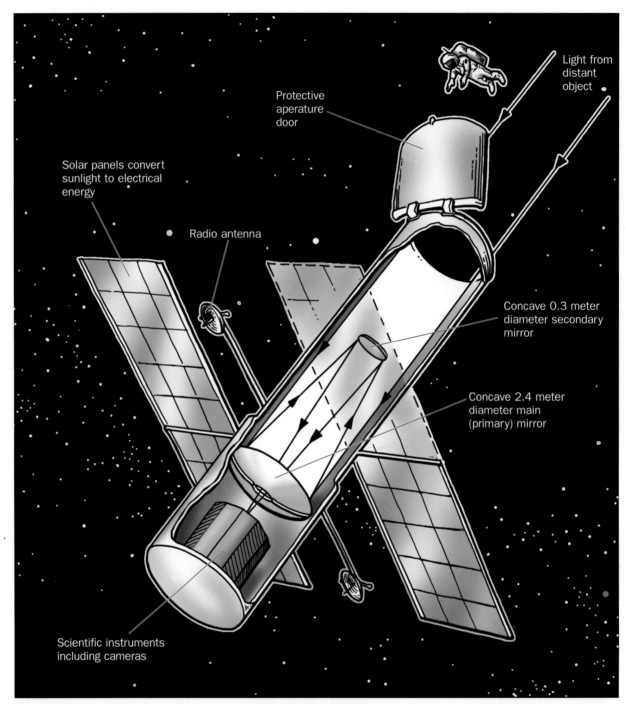

Solar panels convert sunlight to electrical energy

Radio antenna

Protective aperature door

Light from distant object

Concave 0.3 meter diameter secondary mirror

Concave 2.4 meter diameter main (primary) mirror

Scientific instruments including cameras

A look inside the Hubble Space Telescope provides a picture of how it works. What is the role of the giant primary concave mirror?

vibrating. This vibration made the telescope shake slightly. But there was a more serious problem. Images from stars should have been clear pinpoints of light. Instead, these images were blurred and surrounded by a halo of light. It was as if Hubble needed glasses. What was causing this problem?

The Hubble Space Telescope is a reflecting telescope. A giant concave mirror collects light and focuses it onto a camera. The mirror must have exactly the right curve to work properly. Even the tiniest error in its curve would put the telescope out of focus. That's exactly what was wrong with Hubble. When the mirror was ground, it was made 0.0002 centimeters too flat at its edges. This small mistake (less than 1/50 of the width of a human hair) made the stars look blurred. How could this problem be fixed?

Scientists and engineers thought of several ways to solve the problem. They could use

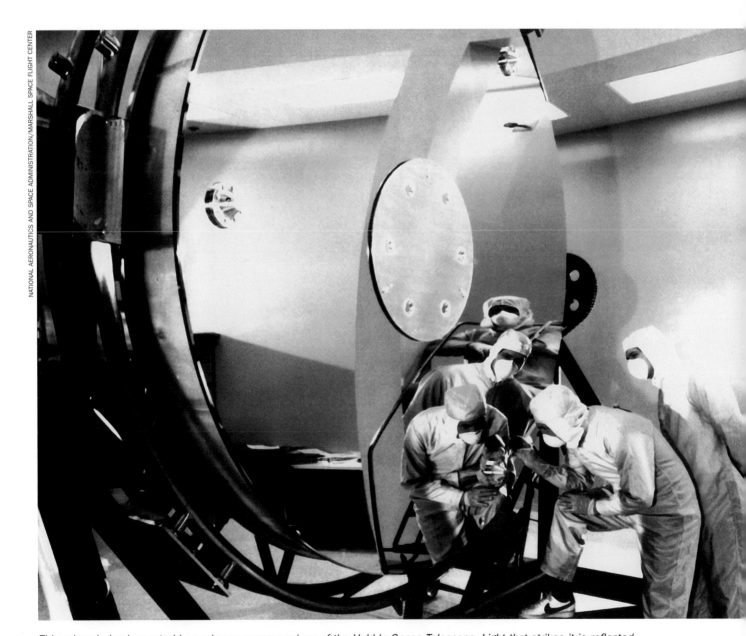

This mirror being inspected is a primary concave mirror of the Hubble Space Telescope. Light that strikes it is reflected into an electronic camera. The image that is detected is transmitted to Earth.

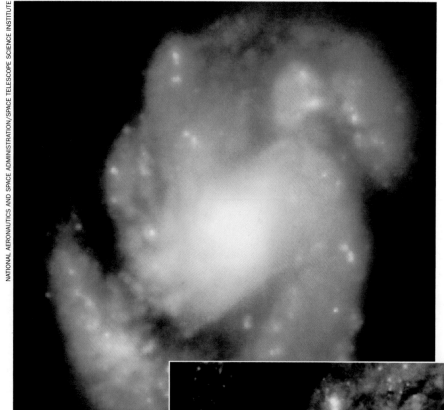

Very small—microscopic, in fact—mistakes in measurements led to errors in the manufacture of the telescope's mirror. Making the mirror too flat at its edges produced a blurring of the image. These pictures show what the same galaxy looked like through the telescope before and after it was repaired.

computers to improve the blurred image. The image would be clearer, but some information would be lost in this process. A better idea would be to add lenses to the telescope. The lenses would correct the telescope's "vision," much like glasses correct human vision.

Second Light

The Hubble Space Telescope had been carefully designed. Engineers had predicted it would need maintenance and upgrading while it was still in orbit. However, nobody had predicted such a major repair!

More than 3 years after Hubble was launched, the crew aboard the space orbiter *Endeavor* docked with the space telescope. They had been thoroughly trained for the most complex space repair mission in history. Working in shifts over the next few days, they spent 35 hours in space. They added a new camera and a

Astronaut Kathryn Thornton unloads the COSTAR (Corrective Optics Space Telescope Axial Replacement) module from the Endeavor orbiter.

NATIONAL AERONAUTICS AND SPACE ADMINISTRATION/JOHNSON SPACE CENTER

The Cone Nebula is a giant finger of gas and dust about 7 light-years long. The light that made this picture left the nebula 2500 years ago and was captured by recently upgraded cameras in the Hubble Space Telescope.

NATIONAL AERONAUTICS AND SPACE ADMINISTRATION, H. FORD (JHU), G. ILLINGWORTH (UCSC/LO), M. CLAMPIN (STScI), G. HARTIG (SRScI) AND THE ACS SCIENCE TEAM

lens module as big as a telephone booth (called COSTAR) to correct Hubble's faulty vision.

Mission completed, they returned to Earth. Would the space telescope work to its full potential? Had the repairs worked? When the computer screen came on, the astronomers saw pinpoints of light—no halos, just clear stars. The eye in space could now see clearly—Hubble's exploration of the universe could continue.

With the experience of the repair mission firmly under their belts, NASA astronauts gained confidence at working on the space telescope. Scientists thought of new ways to improve the eye in space. A recent space mission to upgrade Hubble's cameras allows the space telescope to send even more spectacular pictures back to Earth. The eye in space sees more clearly than ever. As the Hubble Space Telescope explores the universe, it continues to provide all of us back on Earth with a continuing adventure in space. ☐

The Flying Telescope

The bigger and higher the telescope, the better. But putting a telescope into space is an expensive business. Why not have one fly first class on its own private jumbo jet instead? Enter SOFIA—not a person, but a telescope. SOFIA stands for Stratospheric Observatory For Infrared Astronomy. SOFIA is designed to look at astronomical objects by capturing the infrared they emit. SOFIA contains a telescope bigger than Hubble. It is designed to cruise at about 800 kilometers per hour (500 miles per hour) 15,000 meters (49,213 feet) above Earth's surface. This puts it above 99 percent of the infrared-absorbing water vapor found in Earth's atmosphere.

NATIONAL AERONAUTICS AND SPACE ADMINISTRATION

The SOFIA telescope is mounted in a plane and focuses on infrared radiation.

17

Introducing Refraction

We look through transparent materials—solids, liquids, or gases—all the time. Do transparent materials affect the appearance or position of what we observe?

VINCE RODRIGUEZ AT THE NATIONAL AQUARIUM IN BALTIMORE

INTRODUCTION

Have you looked through a window today? For that matter, did you observe your hands while washing them this morning, or look at juice through the side of a glass during breakfast? If you did, you observed light passing from one transparent material to another. What happens when light strikes a transparent object or material like a window or the surface of water? You may already have some ideas.

Here are a few questions to ask yourself. Does all the light striking a transparent object enter it? Does the light entering a transparent object leave it? Does the light entering a transparent object travel in a straight line through it? Does the composition or shape of a transparent object affect the behavior of light? Get ready to share your ideas before you launch into three inquiries that will help test your ideas—and raise other questions—about how light interacts with transparent objects.

OBJECTIVES FOR THIS LESSON

Discuss how light interacts with transparent objects.

Make observations through a transparent block.

Observe and make measurements of a light ray as it interacts with a transparent block.

Use standardized terms to describe the behavior of a light ray as it interacts with a transparent block.

Getting Started

1. Use the questions in the Introduction to help you with your thinking in Steps 2 and 3.

2. Discuss with your group where, in previous lessons, you have observed light interacting with transparent objects. Discuss what you observed in each case.

3. Brainstorm with the class examples of these and other observations you have made of light interacting with transparent objects and materials.

MATERIALS FOR LESSON 17

For you
- 1 copy of Student Sheet 17.2: Shining Light Into a Transparent Block
- 1 copy of Student Sheet 17.3: Measuring Refraction in a Transparent Block

For you and your lab partner
- 1 transparent block
- 1 white screen
- 1 copy of Inquiry Master 17.1: Protractor Paper for Inquiries 17.2 and 17.3
- 1 protractor
- 1 metric ruler, 30 cm (12")
- 1 box of colored pencils
- 1 pair of scissors

For your group
- 1 ray box
- 1 ray box lid
- 1 60-W clear halogen lightbulb
- 1 extension cord
- 1 bulb holder
- 2 narrow-slit ray box masks
- 2 no-slit ray box masks

Inquiry 17.1
Looking Through a Transparent Block

PROCEDURE

1. One member of your group should collect the plastic box of materials. Divide the materials between the pairs in your group. (Your group will share a ray box in Inquiries 17.2 and 17.3.) There is no student sheet for this inquiry. Record your responses in your science notebook.

2. Examine the transparent block. Look through the block from different angles. Discuss what you observe with your partner. Make a list of all your observations in your notebook.

3. Rest the block on top of the page of this book. Record what you observe.

4. Look sideways through the block. Hold your finger up behind the block. Look at your finger through the block and slowly rotate the block from side to side (see Figure 17.1). What do you observe when you rotate the block? Record your observations and share them with your partner.

5. What do you think is happening? Be prepared to share your observations and ideas with the class.

Figure 17.1   *Look at your finger through the block. What do you observe when you rotate the block?*

Inquiry 17.2
Shining Light Into a Transparent Block

PROCEDURE

1. Set up the ray box and white screen so that the side of the ray box at which your pair is working will produce a single ray of light.

2. Use the scissors to cut along the cutout lines on the protractor paper.

3. Place the protractor paper on top of the white screen. The curved side of the protractor diagram should face the mask (see Figure 17.2). It should be no more than 3 centimeters from the ray box.

4. Place the transparent block on the paper so that it is parallel to the ray box with its top edge along the baseline of the protractor paper (see Figure 17.2).

5. Plug in the ray box. Make sure the ray passes through your block.

6. Shine the ray along the 0° line (the normal) of the protractor paper. Observe what happens when the light ray strikes the transparent block.

SAFETY TIP

Do not touch the lightbulb. It gets hot and may burn your fingers.

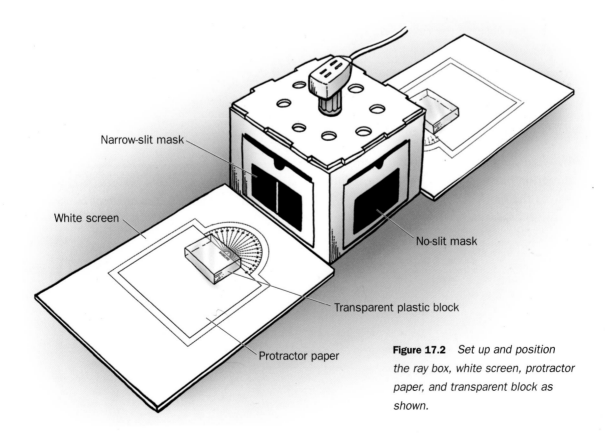

Narrow-slit mask

White screen

No-slit mask

Transparent plastic block

Protractor paper

Figure 17.2 *Set up and position the ray box, white screen, protractor paper, and transparent block as shown.*

A. On Student Sheet 17.2: Shining Light Into a Transparent Block, complete the diagram by recording what you observe. Draw all the rays you observe. Do not forget to draw arrows to show the direction you think the light is traveling.

B. Describe what happens to the ray of light as it strikes the block.

7. *Very slowly* turn the block clockwise on the protractor paper (as shown in Figure 17.3). Carefully observe the behavior of the light as it strikes the rotating block.

C. As you rotate the block, stop about every 15–20° and use a diagram and words to record what you observe.

D. What do you notice about the angle of the reflected ray as you rotate the block?

E. How do your observations fit in with what you know about reflection?

F. Can you observe the ray inside the block?

G. What do you observe about the position and direction of the ray as it leaves the block?

H. What do you think happens to the direction of the light ray as it enters and leaves the block?

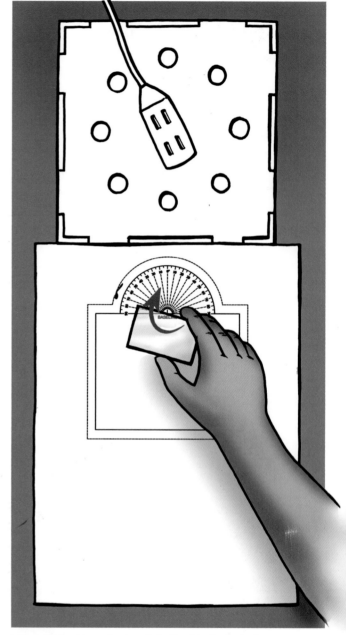

Figure 17.3 *Very slowly rotate the block clockwise.*

8. Read "Reflection and Refraction."

REFLECTION AND REFRACTION

Light changes direction when it reflects off a surface. We call this change in direction reflection. Light also may change direction when it travels from one transparent material into another. (What were the two transparent materials involved in your investigation?) This change in the direction of light is called refraction. Once light has been refracted, it continues in a straight line within that material until it strikes another surface.

I. Where did refraction of the ray take place in this inquiry?

Inquiry 17.3
Measuring Refraction in a Transparent Block

PROCEDURE

1. Reposition the block and protractor paper so that the light ray strikes the block along the 0° line on the protractor paper.

2. *On the protractor paper,* use a colored pencil to draw around the block (see Figure 17.4). Draw lines showing where light enters and leaves the block.

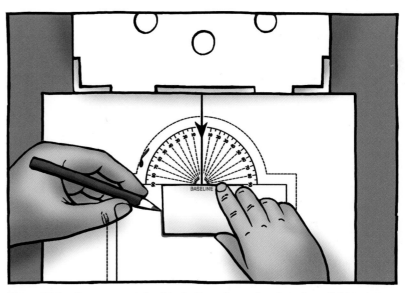

Figure 17.4 *Draw around the block. Draw lines showing where light enters and leaves the block.*

3. Turn *both* the transparent block and protractor paper 20° clockwise (see Figure 17.5). (The front face of the block should still lie along the baseline of the protractor paper.) The light ray now has an angle of incidence of 20°.

4. Use a different colored pencil to draw the rays entering and leaving the block as before.

5. Rotate the block and protractor paper 20° more. Use a third colored pencil to draw the rays.

6. Remove the block from the paper. For each different angle of the incident ray, use the ruler and appropriate colored pencil to draw in the path of the light rays *as they pass through* the block.

A. Transfer what you have recorded onto the three diagrams of blocks on Student Sheet 17.3: Measuring Refraction in a Transparent Block. (You may find it useful to rotate the protractor paper so that the angle of the block's outline matches the angle shown in the diagram.)

7. Compare how light behaved when the block was in the three different positions.

B. Did the light ray entering the block always behave in the same way?

Figure 17.5 *Rotate the transparent block and the protractor paper 20° clockwise. Use a different colored pencil to draw rays entering and leaving the block.*

8. Look at the diagrams you have completed for the blocks with angles of incidence of 20° and 40°.

C. Describe exactly what happens to the light ray as it passes from air into the transparent block at each angle.

D. Describe exactly what happens to the light ray as it passes from the transparent block into the air.

E. How does changing the angle at which the light ray strikes the block affect the position of the ray as it leaves the block?

F. Is there any relationship between the direction of the ray striking the block and the direction of the ray leaving the block?

9. Read "Introducing Refraction."

INTRODUCING REFRACTION

When a ray of light (the incident ray) strikes the transparent block, some light is reflected (the reflected ray) and some light enters and passes through the block. If the ray enters at right angles (along the normal) to the block's surface, the light passes through the block in a straight line. If the ray has a different angle of incidence, the ray bends at the boundary—it is refracted—between the air and the transparent block. The light ray inside the block is called the refracted ray. The angle between the normal and the refracted ray is called the angle of refraction.

The refracted ray travels in a straight line and emerges from the block. At this point, the ray emerges from the block and changes direction again because it has been refracted by passing through the second surface of the block to re-enter the air. This refracted ray is called the emergent ray. Look at the diagram—it shows some of the rays you may have seen entering and leaving the transparent block.

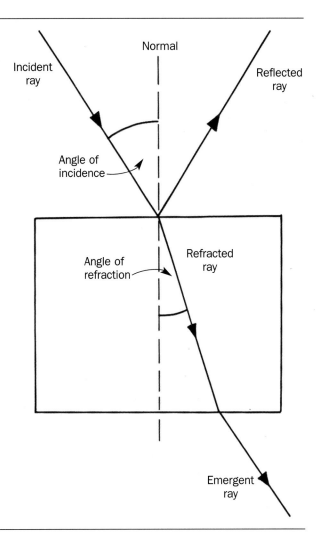

10. On one of the diagrams you completed under A on your student sheet, identify the incident, reflected, refracted, and emergent rays. Label them on your diagram.

G. When light passes into, through, and out of the transparent block, where does refraction occur?

H. When light passes from air into transparent plastic, does it behave in the same way as it does when it passes from transparent plastic into the air? Describe any differences or similarities that occur.

11. Write in values for the angles of incidence on each diagram.

12. Use a protractor to measure the angles (on the protractor paper) of refraction you obtained. Write these in on each diagram.

I. Describe the effect that changing the angle of the incident ray has on the angle of refraction.

SAFETY TIP

Turn off the ray box immediately after you finish using it. Allow the ray box to cool.

REFLECTING ON WHAT YOU'VE DONE

1. Record your responses to the following on Student Sheet 17.3. Be prepared to share your responses with the class.

   A. What is the difference between reflection and refraction?

   B. Write a paragraph summarizing what you have learned about the behavior of light after it strikes and passes through a transparent block. When writing your description, try to use the correct names for the rays and the angles they have to the normal.

2. Review the question bank cards generated in Lesson 1. Can you answer any more of them now? Identify those that you feel comfortable answering.

Refractive Index and
Wet Pants

The water is deeper than it looks. Knowledge of how light is refracted when it passes from water into the air might have saved this hiker the embarrassment of wet pants.

Refraction between the air and this jar of water makes this student look distorted. What causes refraction?

Phew! It's a scorching day, and that creek looks very inviting to a hot, tired hiker. His feet are aching, and he's dying to slip off his stiff hiking boots and thick socks and wade in that nice cool water. In he goes, and . . . Splash! Instead of being up to his ankles, the water is up to his knees. Why was the water much deeper than it appeared—and how will the hiker dry his pants? If only he had paid attention in science class! Why? Because he would have known that the apparent depth of the water was an illusion. Look at the picture of the hiker. Can you see how the hiker's brain was tricked by refraction?

What Causes Refraction?

Light is refracted when it changes speed. Light changes speed when it passes from one transparent material into another. For example, light travels slower in water than in air—about three-quarters as fast. Light therefore bends when it passes from air into water. (Do you remember the nail in water in Lesson 1? Did it appear bent?) The difference between the speed of light in two transparent materials determines how much the light bends as it passes between them. The bigger the difference in the speed of light in the two materials, the more bending, or refraction, takes place when the light passes from one material into another.

Refractive Index

Scientists find it useful to compare the light bending abilities of different transparent materials. They make this comparison using something called the refractive index. The refractive index of a transparent material is defined as the speed of light in a vacuum divided by the speed of light in the transparent material. Each transparent material has a different refractive index.

The slower the speed of light in a material, the higher its refractive index. In a vacuum—where there is no matter to slow down the light—light travels at its fastest speed. The refractive index of a vacuum is 1. This is the lowest refractive index. In glass, light travels much slower, about two-thirds the speed of light in a vacuum. The refractive index for glass is about 1 divided by two-thirds—a refractive index of about 1.5. Table 1 shows refractive indices of a vacuum and of different transparent materials.

In which of these transparent materials does light travel the slowest?

Bird Brains and Fishy Physics

If you know the refractive index of two materials, you can predict which way light will bend when it passes from one to another. Light passing from a material with a lower refractive index to one with a higher refractive index bends toward the normal (just as you observed when light passed from the air into the transparent plastic block).

What happens when light travels in the opposite direction? When light passes from a material with a higher refractive index into one with a lower refractive index (for example, from the transparent plastic block into the air), it is refracted in the opposite direction. The light ray bends away from the normal.

If the hiker had known this, could he have avoided getting his pants wet? Look back at the picture of the soggy hiker. Light reflected from the creek bed travels from water into the air. Air has a lower refractive index than water. As light passed from the water into the air it was

Table 1 Refractive Indices of Some Transparent Materials

Transparent Materials	Refractive Index
Vacuum (A vacuum contains no matter.)	1.00
Air	Slightly higher than 1.00 (1.000293)
Glass	1.53
Diamond	2.42
Transparent plastic	1.50
Water	1.33

refracted away from the normal. This made the water look shallow. The hiker was tricked by refraction!

Some birds that are expert fishers, such as the great blue heron, don't make the mistake the hiker made. They take refraction into account when they lunge underwater for their prey. They must lunge at a position deeper and at an angle different than where the fish appears to be. Did you know that birdbrains were so good at physics?

Now imagine you're a fish looking up from the water into the air. You would have the reverse problem of the hiker or the heron. Light traveling from the air into the water is refracted in the opposite direction, toward the normal. From underwater, objects look farther away than they actually are.

Can you use refractive indices to predict how light will behave when it passes from water to glass? Will a ray of light be refracted toward or away from the normal? ☐

The archerfish squirts water at insects to knock them off overhanging waterside plants. Archerfish have evolved a shooting technique to deal with the refraction that takes place between water and air. Each time the fish shoots a stream of water it takes into account that the insects are nearer, and at a different angle, than they appear.

18
Getting Things Into Focus

No, it's not a Cyclops! How does this transparent object produce this effect?

MOSS PHOTOGRAPHY.COM

INTRODUCTION

Can you recall what happens to light as it enters and leaves a transparent rectangular block? What term did you use to describe this process? Many transparent objects do not have flat sides like the block you investigated in Lesson 17. How do you think light behaves when it strikes transparent objects with curved surfaces? How do such transparent objects affect the appearance of other objects that are viewed through them? In this lesson, you will conduct and design some inquiries to discover the answers to these questions.

OBJECTIVES FOR THIS LESSON

Make observations through transparent objects with curved surfaces.

Classify transparent objects with curved surfaces.

Investigate how light behaves when it passes through transparent objects with curved surfaces.

Getting Started

1. One member of your group should collect the plastic box of materials. Divide the round transparent objects between the pairs in your group so that each pair has three different transparent objects.

2. Examine the objects. Discuss the following with your partner.

Where have you previously seen objects like these?

Do these objects refract light? What evidence do you have for your answer?

Do objects like these have a particular name?

3. Sort the objects into two groups.

What characteristics did you use to sort the objects?

4. Be prepared to share your answers to these questions with the class.

MATERIALS FOR LESSON 18

For you
- 1 copy of Student Sheet 18.1: Examining Images Made by Convex Lenses
- 1 copy of Student Sheet 18.2: Investigating Refraction in Convex Lenses
- 1 copy of Student Sheet 18.3: Investigating a Concave Lens

For you and your lab partner
- 3 transparent objects
- 1 metric ruler, 30 cm (12")
- 1 white screen
- 1 wide-slit ray box mask
- 1 no-slit ray box mask
- 1 comb

For your group
- 1 ray box
- 1 ray box lid
- 1 60-W clear halogen lightbulb
- 1 bulb holder
- 1 extension cord

INTRODUCING LENSES

Transparent objects with curved surfaces like the ones you have just observed are called lenses. Like the block you used in Lesson 17, lenses refract light. Lenses with surfaces that curve outward are called "convex" lenses. Lenses with surfaces that curve inward—like a cave—are called "concave" lenses. Some lenses have a combination of surfaces with different shapes and are named accordingly. For example, a lens with one flat side (or plane) and one convex side is called a "plano-convex" lens. Can you think of any places where you have seen lenses being used?

Inquiry 18.1
Examining Images Made by Convex Lenses

PROCEDURE

1. Place the thicker of the convex lenses on this page. Have your partner hold the ruler so that one end touches the page next to the lens. Keeping your eye at the end of the ruler, pick up the lens and move it slowly toward your eye (see Figure 18.1).

2. Look for any changes in the appearance of the letters on the page as you move the lens. Make any measurements you consider appropriate. Record your responses to A–G on Student Sheet 18.1: Examining Images Made by Convex Lenses.

A. Record your observations and measurements.

Figure 18.1 *Keeping your eye at the end of the ruler, pick up the lens and move it slowly toward your eye. What do you observe through the lens?*

3. Hold the lens about an arm's length from your body. Look through the lens across the room or out the window.

B. Describe what you observe through the thick convex lens.

4. Allow your partner to make the same observations by repeating Steps 1–3.

5. Hold up the white screen so that light from the window (or a brightly lit object) shines though the lens and onto the screen. Move the lens toward and away from the screen (see Figure 18.2).

C. Describe what you observe on the screen.

6. Obtain the clearest image possible on the screen.

D. Record the exact distance (in centimeters or millimeters) from the lens to the screen.

Figure 18.2 *Hold up the white screen so that light shines though the lens and onto the screen. Move the lens toward and away from the screen.*

7. Before answering E, discuss your findings with your group. Here are some suggested points to consider in your discussion.

How did the lens affect the appearance of the size of the letters on the page?

How did the appearance of the letters change as you moved the lens away from the page?

At what distance from the page did the letters look biggest?

What happened to the orientation of the letters as you moved the lens away from the page (and how far from the page did this occur)?

What happened to the size of the letters as you moved the lens away from the page?

What did you observe when you looked at distant objects through the lens?

What did you observe on the screen?

E. List how many images you could make using this lens. For each image, describe its characteristics (magnified or reduced, upright or inverted, real or virtual) and how you made it.

8. Now take out the thinner of the two convex lenses.

F. Investigate the thin convex lens in the same way. Record your observations and measurements.

G. Write a paragraph comparing your results from the two lenses.

9. Be prepared to contribute your observations and ideas to a class discussion on convex lenses.

Inquiry 18.2
Investigating Refraction in Convex Lenses

PROCEDURE

1. Using your knowledge of refraction and your observations from Inquiry 18.1, discuss with your partner how light rays may behave when they enter and leave a convex lens. Be prepared to share your ideas with the class.

2. Set up the apparatus shown in Figure 18.3. (You will work in pairs, but will share a ray box with the other pair in your group.) Record your responses to A–I on Student Sheet 18.2: Investigating Refraction in Convex Lenses.

3. Use the apparatus to investigate what happens to rays of light when they strike each of the two convex lenses.

   A. Design a table for recording your observations and measurements.

4. Discuss your observations with your group. As a group, discuss and then record your answers to the following questions:

   B. Were all the rays that struck a particular lens refracted through the same angle?

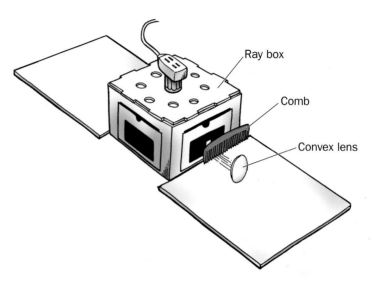

Figure 18.3 *Set up the apparatus as shown. You will need to adjust the position of the comb and lens to get the rays to pass through the lens.*

C. What happened to the light rays after they left the lenses?

D. At what distances did this happen?

E. Compare this distance with the one you measured for D of Inquiry 18.1. Comment on your comparison.

F. How can your observations help you explain the inverted image you obtained on the screen in Inquiry 18.1?

SAFETY TIP

Do not touch the lightbulb. It is hot and may cause painful burns.

5. Read "How a Convex Lens Focuses Light."

6. Use the reader and your observations to answer these questions:

G. Determine the focal lengths of the thick and thin convex lenses.

H. Is there a relationship between focal length and the curvature of the convex lens? If so, what is it?

I. What is the relationship between focal length and the distance at which the lenses produced focused images of distant objects on a screen?

7. Read "How a Convex Lens Forms an Image."

HOW A CONVEX LENS FOCUSES LIGHT

When you moved the lenses toward and away from the screen or the page, you found that you could obtain a clear image with the lenses only in certain positions. This clear image is said to be in focus or focused. The distance between the convex lens and the object when the image of the object comes into focus depends on the shape of the convex lens.

In Inquiry 18.2, you discovered that parallel rays are refracted by a convex lens so that they come together (converge) at a point on the other side of the lens. This point at which light rays converge and cross over is called the focal point of the lens. The distance between the middle of the lens (its optical center) and the focal point is called the focal length of the lens. You can determine the approximate focal length of a lens by measuring the distance between the lens and a focused image of a distant object (for example, the inverted image you observed on the white screen).

Some Important Features of a Convex Lens

Use this diagram to help you understand how a convex lens works.

O *(optical center): Light rays passing through this point do not change direction.*

C *(center of curvature): This point is the center of the sphere of which the lens surface is a part. Your lenses have two centers of curvature, one for each curved surface. Only one center of curvature is shown in this illustration.*

PA *(principal axis): This line connects the center of curvature and the optical center of the lens.*

F *(focal point): This is the point on the principal axis through which all light rays traveling parallel to the principal axis of a convex lens meet.*

f *(focal length): This is the distance between the focal point and the optical center.*

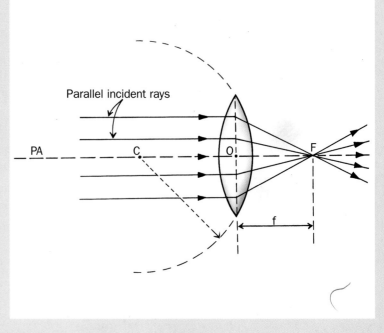

HOW A CONVEX LENS FORMS AN IMAGE

Look at the ray diagram. It shows how an image of a distant object—like the scene outside a window—is focused on the screen by a convex lens.

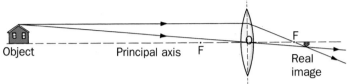

The formation of an image of a distant object by a convex lens

The rays reflected from a distant object— the house—are almost parallel to one another (and to the principal axis). These parallel rays are refracted so that they pass through or near the focal point. Rays passing from the object through the optical center are not refracted. Look closely at the ray diagram. You will notice that the place where these rays cross (only two rays are shown on the diagram) determines where the image is formed. The image is formed just beyond the focal point of the lens. (In fact, for a distant object, the place where the image is formed is very close to the focal point of the lens.) The image is called a "real image" because light reflected from the object really exists and can be detected at this point in space. Because it is a real image it can be projected onto a screen. The image is inverted because the light rays that produce the image have crossed over at the focal point of the lens.

Objects closer to the lens—like the letter A in this ray diagram—are brought into focus farther from the focal point. However, the image is still real and inverted.

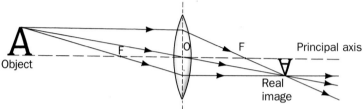

The formation of an image when an object (in this case, the letter A) is closer to a convex lens

This image is the same as the inverted image you may have observed when you looked at a page of your Student Guide through the lenses in Inquiry 18.1.

What would happen if an object were really close to the lens—inside its focal length? Would the image produced be a real or virtual one? Would it look bigger or smaller than the object? Look at the ray diagram below. It explains how a person would see an object (the solid letter A) observed in this way.

The rays appear to come from a point behind the object. The image is magnified, upright, and virtual. Where in the previous lessons have you encountered such an image?

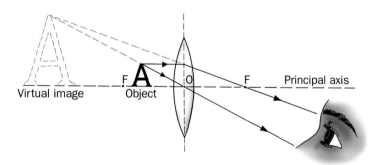

The formation of an image when the object (the solid letter A) is very close to a convex lens (that is, within the focal length of the convex lens)

Inquiry 18.3
Investigating a Concave Lens

PROCEDURE

1. Working with your partner, investigate the image(s) the concave lens can produce.

A. On Student Sheet 18.3: Investigating a Concave Lens, describe the image(s) produced by a concave lens.

2. Predict what will happen if you shine light rays through the lens.

B. Draw a diagram of your prediction.

3. Using the equipment available, devise your own procedure to test your prediction.

C. Record your observations.

4. Discuss your observations with members of another group. Work with them to answer the following questions about the concave lens:

D. What does this lens do to incident light rays?

E. Does this lens have a focal point—a point where the rays come together (or appear to come together) and cross over? If so, can you observe it, or can you suggest where it could be?

F. What are the characteristics of the image produced by a concave lens? (Is it upright or inverted, magnified or reduced, real or virtual?)

5. Share your ideas in a short class discussion about concave lenses, then read "How a Concave Lens Forms an Image."

REFLECTING ON WHAT YOU'VE DONE

1. Discuss with your partner the characteristics of convex and concave lenses.

A. Working with your partner, complete Table 1 on Student Sheet 18.3.

2. Read and discuss with your class "A Colored Blur."

SAFETY TIP

Turn off the ray box immediately after you finish using it. Allow the ray box to cool.

HOW A CONCAVE LENS FORMS AN IMAGE

Look at the ray diagram. It shows how a concave lens forms an image.

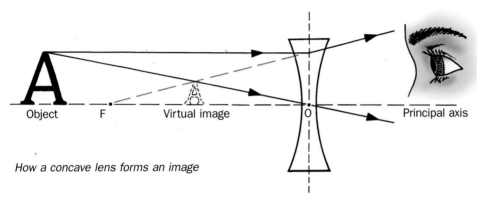

How a concave lens forms an image

As parallel rays from an object pass through the concave lens, they are refracted and diverge. To an observer looking at the object through the lens, the image is smaller than the object. No light from the object is focused where the image appears to be. The image produced by a concave lens is therefore a virtual image. When observing a distant object through a concave lens, the image of the object appears to be very near the focal point of the lens. Concave lenses only produce reduced, upright virtual images.

A Colored Blur

When you used lenses to look at the letters on the page, did you notice something odd about the color of the image? Did you see a colored blur? Have you seen this effect before?

When white light passes from one transparent material to another, the wavelengths that make up the white light are refracted by slightly different amounts. This causes the white light to split into different colors—something that is useful when you are using a prism to observe the spectrum of white light. But what if you want to use a lens to observe a clear, accurately colored image? When light passes through the lens, different colors in the light are refracted by slightly different amounts. These different colors therefore focus at slightly different distances from the lens. This creates a colored blur—called a chromatic aberration—around the image.

Many modern lenses (in cameras and telescopes, for example) are specially designed to reduce chromatic aberrations by making different colors focus at the same point. These lens are called achromatic lenses. (The term "achromatic" means without color.) This photograph shows chromatic aberration produced by an inexpensive hand lens when it is used to observe a printed page.

JEFF MCADAMS, PHOTOGRAPHER, COURTESY OF CAROLINA BIOLOGICAL SUPPLY COMPANY

MOVIE PHYSICS

As the movie theater lights dim, voices hush. In the dark you can hear an occasional cough or the rustle of candy wrappers and smell the aroma of buttered popcorn. The screen lights up. Welcome to the world according to Hollywood—a world of make-believe made from moving images and digital sound. Hold on tightly to your seat. The movie is about to start.

What is the physics behind watching a movie? While a movie character often begins in someone's imagination, the character's image on the screen is a real image. Light rays shined onto the movie screen produce the image we see as a moving picture. But how is such a big, clear, and moving image produced?

Projecting the Best Image

When you made your pinhole camera you projected an image onto a screen. The image was small, dim, and upside down. A projector at the back of the movie theater is a more complex optical device. It uses a very bright light source and lenses to project a big, bright image onto the screen.

Let's see how a movie projector works by following the light from its source in the projector to the image on the movie screen. The film—a long strip of transparent pictures—is positioned in the middle of the projector. Behind the film is a very bright lamp sitting inside a concave reflector. White light from the lamp is concentrated though two lenses—called a condenser—onto the film. The rays emerging from the

In a movie theater, you watch a real image projected onto a screen. How is this done?

A modern movie projector is a complex piece of machinery that combines advanced optics and electronics.

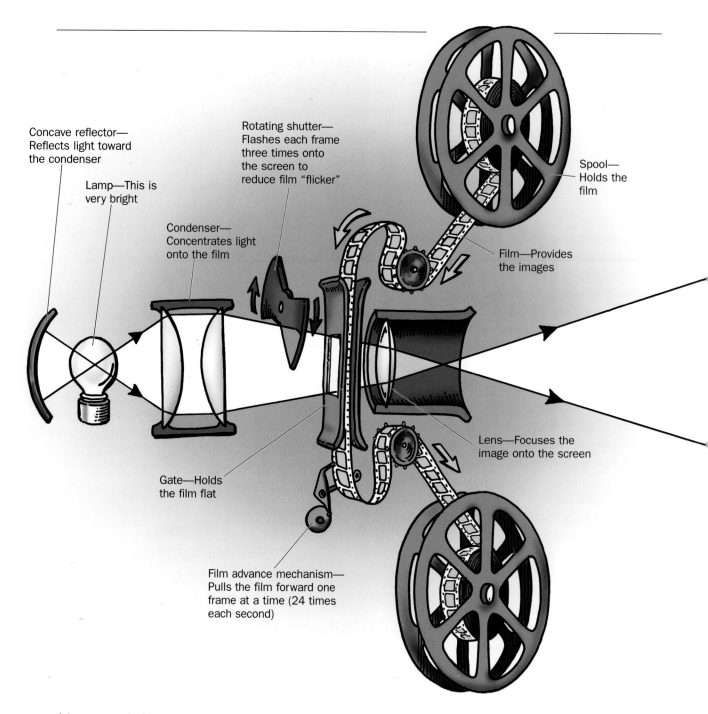

A lot goes on inside a movie projector. Follow the light from the lamp through the film and the lens.

Concave reflector—
Reflects light toward
the condenser

Lamp—This is
very bright

Condenser—
Concentrates light
onto the film

Rotating shutter—
Flashes each frame
three times onto
the screen to
reduce film "flicker"

Spool—
Holds the
film

Film—Provides
the images

Lens—Focuses the
image onto the screen

Gate—Holds
the film flat

Film advance mechanism—
Pulls the film forward one
frame at a time (24 times
each second)

condenser pass through the film. The transparent pictures on the film act like a series of multicolored filters. The filtered light, carrying the image on the film, then passes through a series of lenses that spreads the light out and focuses it onto the movie screen.

Look carefully next time you are in a movie theater. You will see this spreading beam of light emerging from the projector booth. Because the projector is far from the screen at the opposite end of the theater, the light can spread out. When the light strikes the screen, the image produced is therefore many times larger than the original tiny picture on the film. The movie screen then reflects some of the light that forms this image to your eyes.

Making Movies Move

The thousands of images that make up the moving picture we see on the screen are stored on a long piece of transparent film. This film is wound on a reel and runs continuously through the movie projector. The film is fed into the projector upside down and reversed left to right. When light rays shining through the film pass through the lenses of the projector, they cross. The picture on the screen therefore appears to the audience as right-side up.

The projector uses sprocket gears that fit into the small holes in the edges of the film to feed 24 of these separate images past the lens each second. A shutter flashes each of these images onto the screen three times. (This means 72 pictures are projected each second. This flash rate is so fast that our eyes do not notice the images flickering on the screen.) Our eyes and visual system interpret these pictures as moving. Movies are an example of an optical illusion. You will look at optical illusions in more detail in Lesson 24.

Next time you go to a movie, check out the physics of the movie theater. It may prove to be as exciting as the film! ☐

The film is fed into the projector upside down and reversed left-to-right. When inverted by the projector, it appears on the screen in its correct orientation.

19

Modeling Reflection and Refraction

What does the law of reflection have to do with this game?

© JEFF GREENBERG/VISUALS UNLIMITED

INTRODUCTION

In Lesson 7, you modeled light as particles and as waves. Can you remember what represented the particles and waves in these models? In this lesson, you use these models again. This time you are going to see whether they can be used to model how light is reflected and refracted. You first will design experiments that use your models to model the reflection of light from plane, convex, and concave mirrors. Next you will investigate whether the same models can be used to model refraction. You then will compare your observations of the models with the observations you made of light being reflected and refracted. You will use these comparisons to reevaluate the models.

OBJECTIVES FOR THIS LESSON

Design ball bearing (particle) and water wave models of reflection of light from plane and curved mirrors.

Observe ball bearing (particle) and water wave models of refraction.

Compare and evaluate the ball bearing (particle) and water wave models with the behavior of light.

Getting Started

1. With your group, use your notes from Lesson 7 and the following questions to help you review the models that you used to model light as waves and particles:

What did you use to represent light waves or particles?

What aspects of light's behavior did you model?

How did you compare the two models?

2. Participate in a class review of these models.

MATERIALS FOR LESSON 19

For you

1 copy of Student Sheet 19.1: Can Particles Model Reflection From a Plane Mirror?

1 copy of Student Sheet 19.2: Using Particles To Model Reflection From Curved Mirrors

1 copy of Student Sheet 19.3: Using Waves To Model Reflection

1 copy of Student Sheet 19.4: Modeling Refraction

1 copy of Student Sheet 19.5: Assessment Review: Part 2

1 copy of Student Sheet 19.6: Sample Assessment Questions for Part 2

For your group

15 ball bearings (in a resealable plastic bag)

1 transparent tray

1 metric ruler, 30 cm (12″)

1 straight metal barrier

1 curved plastic barrier

1 cardboard tube

1 piece of modeling clay

1 piece of card

1 copy of Inquiry Master 19.1: Protractor Paper for Lesson 19

2 wooden blocks

1 wooden dowel

1 folding lamp

4 AA batteries

1 transparent cup

1 sheet of white paper

Inquiry 19.1
Can Particles Model Reflection From a Plane Mirror?

PROCEDURE

1. One member of your group should collect the plastic box of materials.

2. Working as a group, set the transparent tray on the table. Place the metal barrier in the tray as shown in Figure 19.1.

3. Tilt the cardboard tube to an angle of about 30°. Roll one ball bearing down the tube so that it strikes the barrier (see Figure 19.1).

4. Discuss with your group how the simple activity you have just done *could be adapted* to investigate whether the ball bearing you used follows the law of reflection.

5. Using the materials provided, devise a procedure to model the reflection of light from a plane mirror.

6. Discuss the type and quantity of data you need to collect. Devise a table for your data.

7. Outline your procedure on Student Sheet 19.1: Can Particles Model Reflection From a Plane Mirror?

8. Use your procedure to collect data. Record your data and observations.

9. Discuss your results with your group. Record any conclusions/comments you may have about the model. Be prepared to share your procedures, observations, and data with the class.

Figure 19.1 *Roll the ball bearing down the cardboard tube while holding the tube at a 30° angle.*

Inquiry 19.2
Using Particles To Model Reflection From Curved Mirrors

PROCEDURE

1. Use the materials provided to devise and conduct an inquiry with your group to model the reflection of light from curved mirrors.

2. Record your procedure, data, and observations on Student Sheet 19.2: Using Particles To Model Reflection From Curved Mirrors.

3. Discuss your results with your group. Record any conclusions/comments you have about the model on the student sheet. Be prepared to share your procedures, observations, and data with the class.

4. Return the ball bearings to the plastic bag and seal the bag.

Inquiry 19.3
Using Waves To Model Reflection

PROCEDURE

1. While your teacher reviews how to use the ripple tank apparatus, think about how you can use this apparatus to model the reflection of light.

2. Working with your group, use the ripple tank to model the reflection of light off plane, convex, and concave mirrors.

3. Record your procedure, data, observations, conclusions, and comments about the model on Student Sheet 19.3: Using Waves To Model Reflection.

4. Discuss with your group how the behavior of the model compares with the behavior of light rays striking these types of mirrors. Be prepared to share your ideas with the class.

SAFETY TIP

Make sure the battery box of the lamp is outside of the tray and does not touch the water.

Inquiry 19.4
Modeling Refraction

PROCEDURE

1. Spend a few minutes reviewing the inquiries you have conducted on refraction.

2. Discuss the following questions with your group:

Why is light refracted when it passes from one transparent material to another?

What determines the direction—toward or away from the normal—in which light is refracted?

3. Set up the apparatus as shown in Figure 19.2.

4. Roll one ball bearing down the ramp. Make observations. Repeat this procedure as many times as you consider necessary to obtain a valid result. Record your responses for this inquiry on Student Sheet 19.4: Modeling Refraction.

A. What happens to the speed of the ball bearing as it rolls over the folded card?

B. The denser a transparent material, the higher its refractive index and the slower the speed of light as it passes through it. For example, light travels faster in less dense air than it does in denser transparent plastic. Which part(s) of this model represents a less dense material (like air), and which part(s) represents a more dense material (like transparent plastic)?

C. Record what happens to the direction of the ball bearings as they are rolled along the normal line.

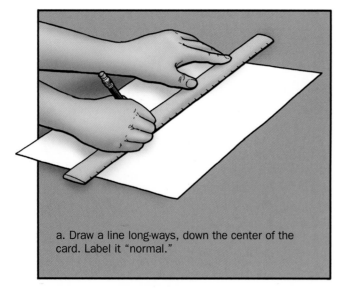

a. Draw a line long-ways, down the center of the card. Label it "normal."

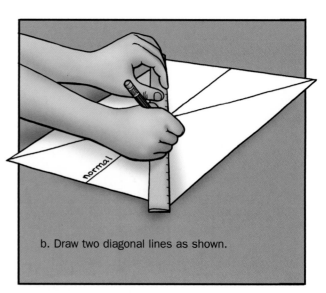

b. Draw two diagonal lines as shown.

Figure 19.2 *Set up the apparatus as shown using the diagrams labeled a–d as a guide.*

5. Realign the v-ramp so that it lies along one of the diagonal lines you have drawn. Repeat Step 4.

D. Record what happens to the direction of the ball bearings as they are rolled along the diagonals.

6. Use the following question to help you comment on your observations:

E. How does the behavior of the ball bearing model compare with the behavior of light?

7. Watch carefully as your teacher demonstrates water waves passing over a transparent block.

F. Draw on the diagrams on Student Sheet 19.4 what you observe occurring in the ripple tank as waves travel over the transparent block.

8. Discuss with your group and then answer these questions (be prepared to share your answers with the class):

G. What evidence (if any) is there that the waves are being refracted?

H. Can you explain your observations and compare them with the behavior of light?

9. Dismantle your ripple tank. Pour the water out of the tray. Dry the tray with a paper towel. Return all the materials to the plastic box.

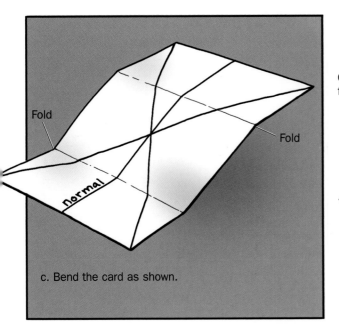

c. Bend the card as shown.

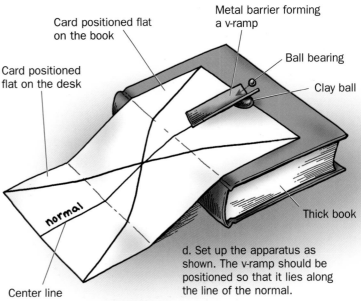

Card positioned flat on the book

Metal barrier forming a v-ramp

Ball bearing

Clay ball

Card positioned flat on the desk

Thick book

Center line

normal

d. Set up the apparatus as shown. The v-ramp should be positioned so that it lies along the line of the normal.

REFLECTING ON WHAT YOU'VE DONE

1. Discuss with your group your observations and conclusions from Inquiries 19.1–19.4.

A. Summarize your observations in Table 1 on Student Sheet 19.4.

2. Review your completed Table 1 and the Table 1 you completed on Student Sheet 7.2 in Lesson 7. Discuss these questions with your group (be prepared to contribute your ideas to a class discussion):

Which of these models best models light?

Do you think both models could be useful in helping to explain how light behaves?

3. Based on your experiences in Lesson 7 and this lesson and using what you have read, write a paragraph that answers this question:

B. Do you that think light behaves like waves, like particles, or like both waves and particles?

4. Read "The Greatest Scientific Argument of the Millennium?"

5. Review the question bank cards generated in Lesson 1. Can you answer any more of them now? Identify those you feel comfortable answering.

The Greatest Scientific Argument of the Millennium?

Why do transparent soap bubbles display these colors? Thomas Young explained this phenomenon in terms of light waves interfering with each other.

Scientists often debate ideas or theories for long periods of time. Sometimes more than one theory fits the facts. This is the case with the nature of light. The result has been a reasoned argument and debate that has lasted over 200 years.

Particles or Waves?

Until the 1670s, people were very confused about what light was. At about that time, two scientists came up with different models to describe and explain light. You have already

heard of one of these scientists—Isaac Newton (1642–1727). Newton suggested that light consisted of streams of particles moving at very high speeds. He called these particles "corpuscles" and used this model to explain the fact that light travels in straight lines. Newton's model could explain how light formed shadows, bounced off mirrors, and shined through the vacuum of space. He suggested that the different colors that make up white light were different particles.

For Newton to be able to explain refraction in terms of particles, light would have to travel faster in water or glass than it does in air. (We now know that light passing from air to water or glass slows down.) However, as you have read, at that time nobody could accurately determine the speed of light in air or in any other transparent material. So nobody could tell if Newton's theory best explained refraction.

At about the same time, another scientist, Christian Huygens (1629–1695), had a different explanation. Huygens suggested that light moved like waves traveling across the surface of a pond. He explained color by suggesting that each color was a different wavelength. According to Huygens, refraction occurred because light traveled slower in transparent materials such as water or glass than it did in air.

Huygens's theory of the nature of light was quite different from Newton's explanation. Both theories, however, could explain all the experimental data on refraction that was then available. As new discoveries were made and new data became available, whose theory would ultimately be correct?

Most scientists preferred Newton's idea. Some were betting on his reputation as the greatest scientist of all time. Others couldn't see how Huygens's light waves could travel through a vacuum. After all, how could you have waves in nothing? For more than a century, Newton's corpuscles were in and Huygens's waves were out.

Then along came Thomas Young with a new type of experiment. In 1801, Young discovered that it was possible for two beams of light to interfere with each other and result in different colors or even darkness. He used this idea to explain why transparent materials such as oil films and soap bubbles often look multicolored.

Young called this process "interference" and explained it in terms of "out-of-step" waves interacting with each other. That is, light waves (or other waves) traveling in the same or different directions in the same space disturbed each other. (Try this tonight in the bathtub.) For example, the crest of one wave would cancel or partly cancel the trough of another wave. Young theorized that this activity apparently resulted in some colors being enhanced and others being cancelled out altogether.

Other new discoveries were beginning to make waves look like a better model for light. Many invisible forms of light were being found, all of which could be explained as different wavelengths in the continuous electromagnetic spectrum.

Eventually, waves became the number-one theory. Had Newton at last been proven wrong? Was the debate over? That would be too simple! At the turn of the 20th century, German scientist Max Planck (1858–1947) was studying how hot objects gave off electromagnetic radiation. He discovered that these hot objects did

Max Planck suggested that, although light had many of the characteristics of waves, it also behaved like packets of energy. Were these packets of energy the same as Isaac Newton's corpuscles?

not give off light energy continuously, but rather as packets of specific amounts of light energy (rather like the difference between integer and real numbers). He called these packets of energy "quanta."

This new evidence stirred up the debate even more, and attracted some of the world's greatest scientific minds. One of these scientists was Albert Einstein (1879–1955). Einstein used the idea of light as packets of energy to explain how light can knock electrons off the surface of some metals to produce an electric current. He called these packets of light energy "photons." Were these the same as Newton's corpuscles? Not exactly.

The Dual Nature of Light Revealed

Einstein was not reviving Newton's 200-year-old idea. Instead, he was suggesting that light behaved like both particles and waves. He described light as being waves that come in discrete packages, each containing a fixed amount of energy. This theory explained the existing data better because it clarified why light sometimes behaved like waves and sometimes like particles. Light had dual characteristics—some particle-like and some wave-like. The riddle of the nature of light had taken a new turn, and neither Newton nor Huygens had won or lost the debate. ☐

Newton (left) suggested that light consisted of streams of moving particles. Huygens (right) took the view that light moved like waves. More recently, scientists like Einstein (center) have suggested that light has the characteristics of both.

20

Part 2 Assessment—What Do You Know About the Characteristics and Behavior of Light?

Make sure you carefully record your observations and data.

INTRODUCTION

This lesson is the assessment for Part 2: Reflection and Refraction. It also includes some questions that require you to apply knowledge and skills you acquired in Part 1: The Nature of Light. The assessment is in two sections. You will work by yourself to complete both sections. In Section A, you will conduct an inquiry into lenses. You will make observations and take measurements, and collect, record, and interpret data. In Section B, you will answer multiple-choice and short-answer questions. Some of these questions will require you to use your knowledge and skills to interpret diagrams, data tables, and experiments. You and your teacher will use the results of this assessment to evaluate how well you can apply the knowledge, concepts, and skills you have acquired in the first two parts of the module.

OBJECTIVES FOR THIS LESSON

Identify the lenses in a hand lens.

Make observations through two lenses.

Identify the characteristics of some images.

Determine the approximate focal length of two lenses.

Getting Started

1. Your teacher will inform you when you will do each section of the assessment and how long you will have for each section.

2. In both sections your work will be assessed partly on your layout, labeling, and drawing of data tables and diagrams.

MATERIALS FOR LESSON 20

For you

1 copy of Student Sheet 20.1: Section A— Performance Assessment: Examining a Hand Lens

1 copy of Student Sheet 20.2: Section B—Written Assessment Question Sheet

1 copy of Student Sheet 20.3: Section B—Written Assessment Answer Sheet

1 hand lens

1 metric ruler, 30 cm (12″)

1 white screen

Section A—Performance Assessment

Inquiry 20.1
Examining a Hand Lens

PROCEDURE

Directions Read these instructions before you start working. Record your responses to A–F on Student Sheet 20.1: Section A—Performance Assessment: Examining a Hand Lens. Record any measurements you make using metric units (m, cm, or mm).

1. Examine your hand lens.

   A. What name would you give to the shape of the lenses found in your hand lens?

2. First hold your hand lens exactly 1 cm from the print on this page. Next hold your hand lens exactly 7 cm from the page. At each distance, *keeping your eye level with the end of the ruler,* make observations through the large-diameter and the small-diameter lens.

   B. Record your observations in Table 1 on Student Sheet 20.1.

   C. What evidence is there that these lenses refract different colors or wavelengths of light by slightly different amounts?

3. Your teacher will direct your attention to some distant objects. Use the large-diameter lens to project an image of a distant object onto the white screen.

   D. What characteristics does this image have?

4. Use the materials you have to determine the *approximate* focal length of each of these lenses.

   E. Use a labeled diagram and/or write a paragraph describing the procedure you used to determine the approximate focal length of these lenses.

   F. Record your results.

Section B—Written Assessment

Your teacher will outline the procedure for taking Section B of the assessment.

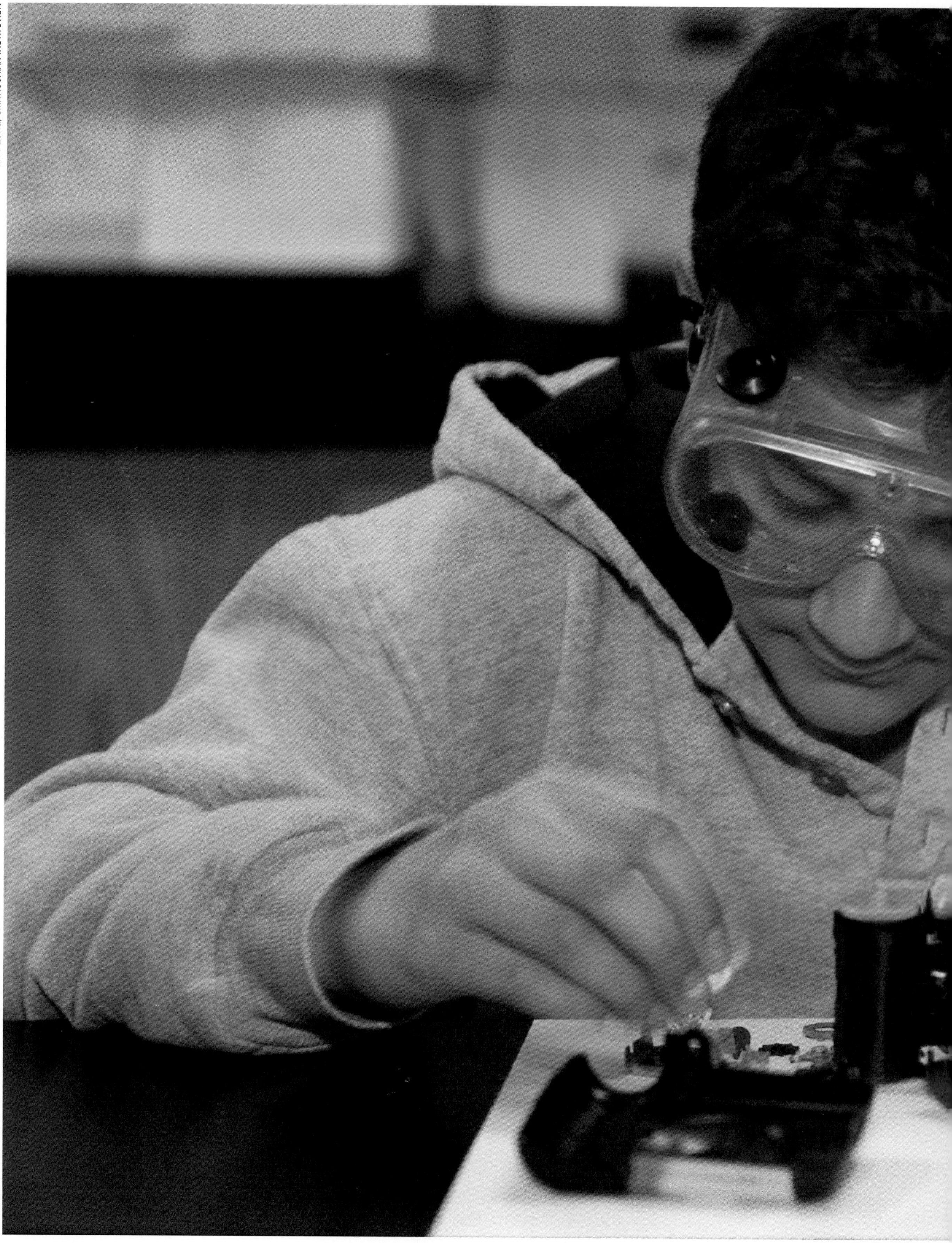

ERIC LONG, SMITHSONIAN INSTITUTION

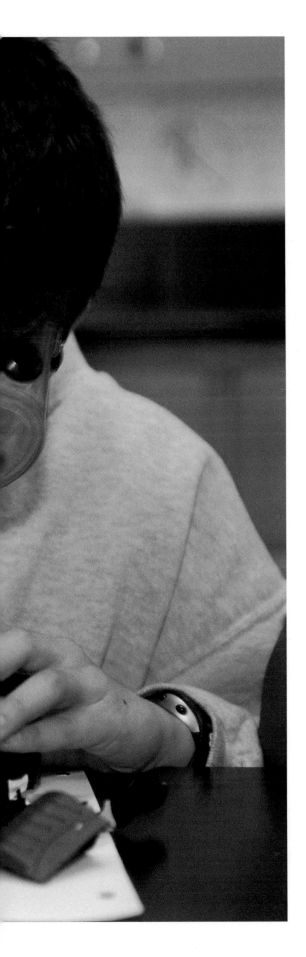

PART 3 Using Light

21
Starting the Anchor Activity

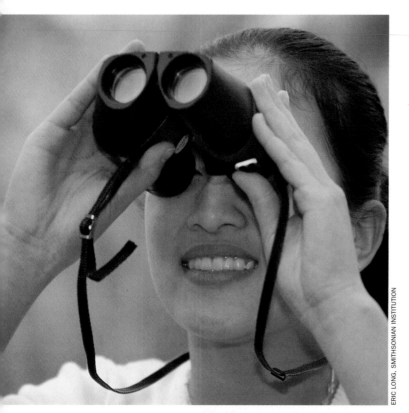

What type of optical device is this student using? Can you find out how it works?

ERIC LONG, SMITHSONIAN INSTITUTION

INTRODUCTION

In this lesson, you will begin the Anchor Activity. You will work on this activity over the next few weeks. What is an Anchor Activity? It is a short project that gives you the opportunity to apply what you have learned in the module to the world around you. In this Anchor Activity, you will select an optical device to examine in more detail. You will investigate what it is used for, how it works, what components are used to make it, and the history of its development. You will use the library, the Internet, and other resources to conduct your research. You will then use the information you collect to make a presentation to the class (supported by a visual aid you have made) about the optical device you select. The work you do for this Anchor Activity will be an important part of your grade for this module. You will be given several homework assignments and a small amount of class time to do this work. However, you will do most of it on your own time. At the end of the module, two to three class periods will be used for Anchor Activity presentations.

OBJECTIVES FOR THIS LESSON

Select an optical device to research.

Research the device you have chosen.

Create a visual aid to support an oral presentation about the device you have chosen.

Give an oral presentation on the device you have chosen.

Getting Started

1. What do you think is meant by the term "optical device"?

2. Share your ideas with the class.

3. Can you think of any optical devices you use? Do you know of any others? As your class compiles a list of optical devices, record the list in your science notebook.

MATERIALS FOR LESSON 21

For you

1 copy of Student Sheet 21.1: Looking at Optical Devices
1 copy of Student Sheet 21.2: Anchor Activity Schedule
Masking tape
Index cards

Inquiry 21.1
Looking at Optical Devices

PROCEDURE

1. Working with your group, examine the optical devices that have been placed around the room. Use the observations you make and the information you collect to make short notes about each device in Table 1 on Student Sheet 21.1: Looking at Optical Devices.

2. Be prepared to share with the class the information about the devices that you have examined.

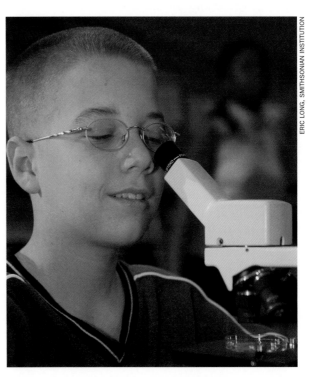

What is this optical device used for? Which components in the device are used to manipulate light? What do these components do?

Inquiry 21.2
Introducing the Anchor Activity

PROCEDURE

1. After your teacher gives you Student Sheet 21.2: Anchor Activity Schedule, tape it in the front of your science notebook. You will need to refer to it as you work on the Anchor Activity. Follow it carefully.

2. Follow along as your teacher reviews the Anchor Activity Guidelines.

Anchor Activity Guidelines

PROCEDURE

Part 1: Choosing an Optical Device

1. You (and you partner, if you are working in pairs) will choose an optical device to study. You may choose one from the class list of optical devices or identify one of your own.

2. Discuss your choice with your teacher. You may be asked to choose another device if your teacher thinks the choice is inappropriate (perhaps because it is too difficult or too many other pairs have chosen it).

3. Review the information in Step 4. If you are working with a partner, decide how you will divide the work.

4. The information you gather will be divided into three sections. As you gather information, write your notes under these headings:

Function
Answer these questions:
What does the device do?

What is it used for?

How Does the Device Work?
Answer these questions:
What does it do to light and how does it do it?

Does it use lenses, mirrors, prisms, or other optical components?

What role do these optical components play in the device?

How do the components work together to make the device work?

Try to produce a labeled diagram showing how it works.

History and Development of the Device
Try to answer these questions:
Was it invented?

If so, by whom?

When and where did it first appear?

How was it developed into its present form?

Part 2: Finding Resources and Writing an Outline

1. To help with planning your presentation, write an outline of your investigation (see Figure 21.1). Your outline should use the headings provided in Step 4 of Part 1.

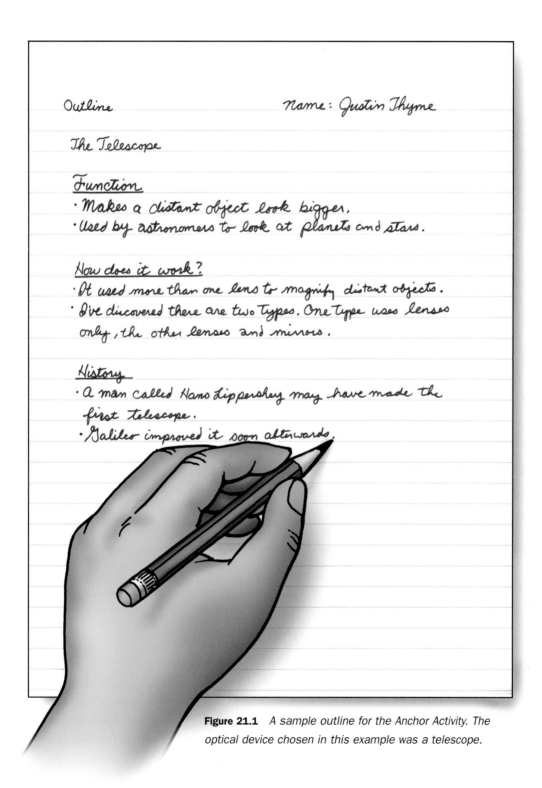

Outline   Name: Justin Thyme

The Telescope

Function
· Makes a distant object look bigger.
· Used by astronomers to look at planets and stars.

How does it work?
· It used more than one lens to magnify distant objects.
· I've discovered there are two types. One type uses lenses only, the other lenses and mirrors.

History
· A man called Hans Lippershey may have made the first telescope.
· Galileo improved it soon afterwards.

Figure 21.1   *A sample outline for the Anchor Activity. The optical device chosen in this example was a telescope.*

2. As you collect information, record your sources in a bibliography. The bibliography can include sources such as books, CD-ROMs, DVDs, videotapes, TV programs, and magazines. It should include at least one Web site and one book (other than an encyclopedia). A sample bibliography is shown in Figure 21.2.

3. Hand in your outline and a copy of your bibliography on separate sheets of paper by the due date on the schedule. Your teacher will use this information to help you make sure your research is heading in the right direction.

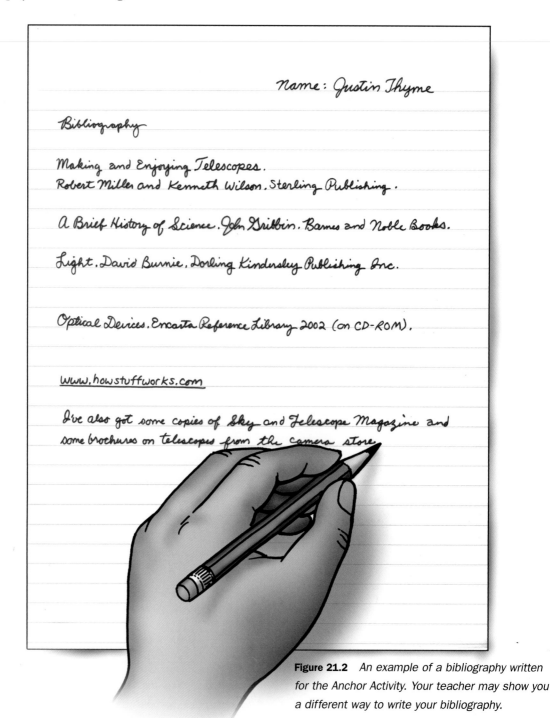

Name: Justin Thyme

Bibliography

Making and Enjoying Telescopes.
Robert Miller and Kenneth Wilson. Sterling Publishing.

A Brief History of Science. John Gribbin. Barnes and Noble Books.

Light. David Burnie. Dorling Kindersley Publishing Inc.

Optical Devices. Encarta Reference Library 2002 (on CD-ROM).

www.howstuffworks.com

I've also got some copies of Sky and Telescope Magazine and some brochures on telescopes from the camera store.

Figure 21.2 *An example of a bibliography written for the Anchor Activity. Your teacher may show you a different way to write your bibliography.*

Part 3: Preparing Your Presentation

1. Prepare your presentation. You will give a 3-minute oral presentation supported by at least one visual aid. Your visual aids can be a poster, Web page, computer (PowerPoint™) or flashcard presentation, or model. Your teacher will outline some points to think about when making your visual aid.

2. Design your visual aid carefully. If you make a poster, be sure it is clearly labeled and does not contain too much information.

3. Create your visual aid.

4. Practice your oral presentation. Ask your parents, teacher, or friends to suggest ways to improve your presentation. Follow these suggestions:

- If working with a partner, make sure you design your presentation so that you both contribute equally to the presentation.
- Refer frequently to the visual aid as you give your presentation.
- If you get nervous when speaking or have a bad memory, make short notes (not complete sentences) on index cards to use during your presentation.
- Make sure your voice can be heard clearly in the back of the room.

Think carefully about how you design your visual aid.

5. Table 21.1 shows the rubric your teacher will use to score your presentation. Use this rubric to help you plan your presentation so that you obtain a high score.

Table 21.1 Scoring Rubric for the Anchor Activity Presentation

Section	What You Should Include	Points awarded	Total Points
Content	**Function** Provide an accurate description of what your optical device does or what it is used for.	5	5
	How does it work? Explain how the device works. How do the different parts of the device work together to perform its function?	10	10
	History and Development When was the device first used? Who developed it? How was it improved?	5	5
Presentation	Speaking loudly and clearly Using your visual aid as you present Organizing your presentation	3 3 4	10
Visual Aid	Using a layout and design appropriate to your visual aid Labeling diagrams, tables, and pictures Originality of materials	5 5 5	15
Bibliography	Include at least five complete references, with at least one Web site and one book (other than an encyclopedia)	5	5
		Total	**50**

Part 4: Presenting Your Anchor Activity

1. Your teacher will tell you the day on which you will make your presentation. Be sure you are prepared.

2. You will have only 3 minutes to make your presentation.

3. Speak clearly. If you are working with a partner, make sure you both contribute equally to the presentation. Don't forget to refer to your visual aid as you make your presentation.

4. After your presentation, hand in your visual aid and the final version of your bibliography.

REFLECTING ON WHAT YOU'VE DONE

1. Discuss with your group which of the presentations that you observed was the most interesting and which was presented best. Try to identify the reasons for your choice(s).

2. How do you think your presentation could have been improved? Make a short list of these improvements in your science notebook.

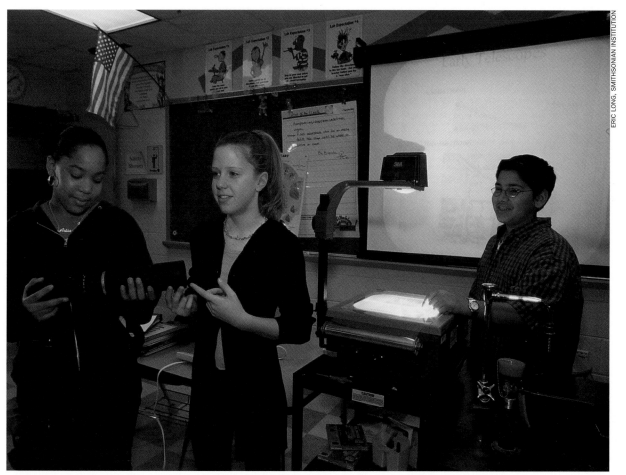

ERIC LONG, SMITHSONIAN INSTITUTION

When making a presentation, use your visual aid to help you explain how your optical device works.

Optics in Action—Digital Data and Amazing Music

What is 1.2 millimeters thick, 12 centimeters in diameter, and can hold the same amount of information as a book 65,000 pages long? You may be surprised to discover you have a few of these at home. But you may be using them for a different purpose.

The item in question is a compact disc, or CD. The most common uses of these shiny disks include storing music, movies—DVDs, similar to CDs—and computer data. CDs store all of these in digital form. What does this mean and how do CDs work?

Look at this close-up photo of a CD. It was taken using a microscope. Can you see the small marks in the disk? These marks are pits and flats arranged in a spiral track on the disk. The track on the CD is thinner than a human hair and about 5 kilometers long. As the CD spins (many hundreds of times each minute), a laser beam follows these tracks and scans these pits and flats. The pits and flats are a form of code. The flats are read as a 1 (on) and the pits as a 0 (off). This 1 and 0, or on-off code, is called a binary, or digital, code. This code is used to store information on the CD. ☐

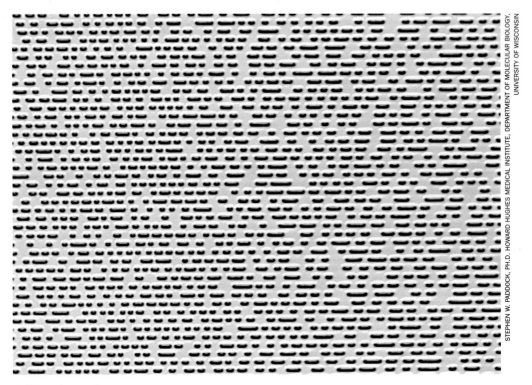

A CD under a microscope

Vinyl records were widely used to play music. Ask a parent or grandparent what an LP was. How fast did it spin? What was the name of the first record they bought?

Listening to Music the Analog Way

Ask one of your parents how they listened to music and they would probably say they used vinyl records or cassette tapes.

Both records and tapes store information in analog form. What does this mean? Analog signals are replicas (that is, copies) of the original. For example, the wiggly shapes of the grooves in a vinyl record vary with the strength and nature of the signal. Vinyl records can be played (very quietly) using just a needle! But when you play a CD, the digital code on the CD must be decoded before it can be converted into music.

Inside an Audio CD Player

One job of a CD player is to keep a laser targeted on the tracks on the spinning CD. The laser sits below the CD and aims at the track starting from the center of the disk. The light from the laser is reflected from the shiny surface of the CD. A component called a photodetector also sits under the CD. It detects whether the laser was reflected from a flat or scattered from a pit. It turns these digital light signals into electrical signals and sends these signals to a microprocessor. The microprocessor decodes the signal into music.

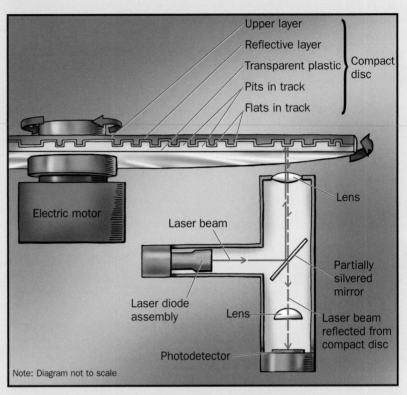

Upper layer
Reflective layer
Transparent plastic
Pits in track
Flats in track
Compact disc

Lens

Electric motor

Laser beam

Partially silvered mirror

Laser diode assembly

Lens

Laser beam reflected from compact disc

Photodetector

Note: Diagram not to scale

A CD player uses a laser to read the information on a CD.

JEFF MCADAMS, PHOTOGRAPHER, COURTESY OF CAROLINA BIOLOGICAL SUPPLY COMPANY

A CD player converts a digital code into music. What's your preference, Mozart or rap?

LIGHT IN STEP— A LASER COMPONENT

Lasers produce light. What is the difference between light from a laser and light from a lightbulb? There are a number of differences. You know that light from a lightbulb is of many different wavelengths or colors. Light from a laser is only one wavelength. A particular laser produces only one color of light—it is mono-chromatic. Light waves leaving a lightbulb are released at random. The waves are therefore out of step with each other. Light waves from a laser are in step with each other. These in-step waves are said to be coherent. Finally, because the waves are all in step, the laser light doesn't spread out as much from its source as light from a lightbulb. This is why laser light is often referred to as a laser beam. The illustration below summarizes the difference between light from these two sources.

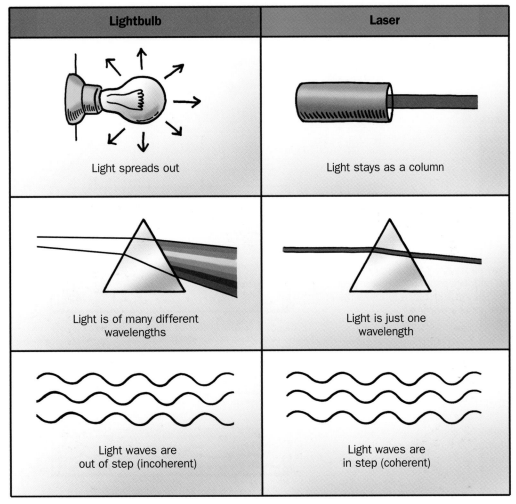

Lightbulb	Laser
Light spreads out	Light stays as a column
Light is of many different wavelengths	Light is just one wavelength
Light waves are out of step (incoherent)	Light waves are in step (coherent)

Unlike light waves from other sources, light from a laser doesn't spread out much. The light waves from a laser are all the same wavelength and are in step with one another.

Lasers take a variety of forms but the way they work is very similar. Some lasers used for research into nuclear energy or as weapons are the size of buildings; others are small enough to fit inside a grain of salt! Inside a CD player, laser light is made inside a component called a laser diode—less than 1 centimeter long. Laser diodes are solid-state lasers. This means they are made from layers of different solids. The laser diode shown has three layers. Examine the diagram carefully.

The laser diode is designed so that its middle layer makes light of a certain wavelength when electrical energy is passed across the layers. Mirrors at the ends of the middle layer of the laser diode stop most of this light from

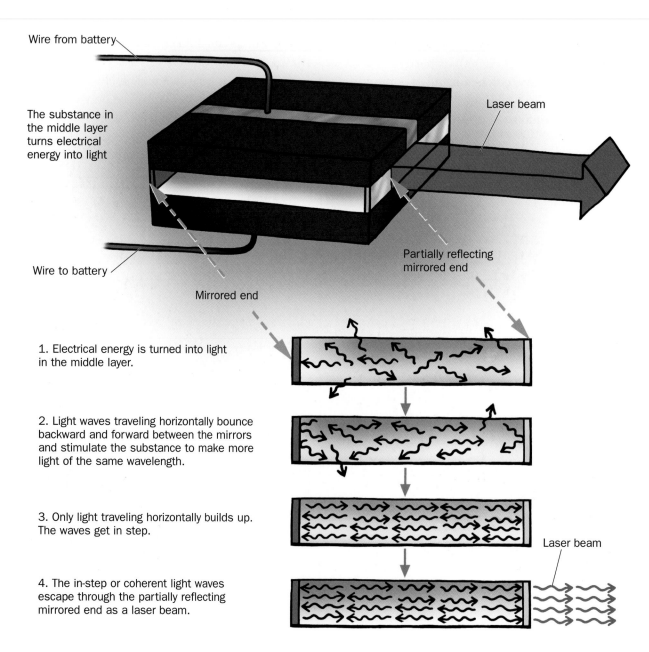

Wire from battery

The substance in the middle layer turns electrical energy into light

Laser beam

Wire to battery

Mirrored end

Partially reflecting mirrored end

1. Electrical energy is turned into light in the middle layer.

2. Light waves traveling horizontally bounce backward and forward between the mirrors and stimulate the substance to make more light of the same wavelength.

3. Only light traveling horizontally builds up. The waves get in step.

Laser beam

4. The in-step or coherent light waves escape through the partially reflecting mirrored end as a laser beam.

*In a laser diode, electrical energy is used to cause a substance to make light. This light is then used to make more light of the same wavelength. "Laser" stands for "**L**ight **A**mplification by **S**timulated **E**mission of **R**adiation."*

escaping. The light bounces backward and forward between the mirrors. As it bounces back and forth it stimulates the atoms that make up the substance in the middle layer to release more light. This additional light is identical in wavelength to the original light. This light is all traveling in the same direction and has the same wavelength. These light waves are all in step. Eventually, many of the light waves bouncing back and forth get in step with one another—rather like water waves going backward and forward in a bathtub.

The light builds up—is amplified—to such a high intensity that even the small fraction of light that does escape through a partially reflecting mirrored surface (like the half-silvered glass you used in Lesson 14) at one end of the diode is still very bright. This light escapes as a laser beam.

In other lasers, laser light is made within crystals or gases. Different types of lasers produce light of different wavelengths. Laser light is used when a compact and intense light source is needed. For example, delicate surgery or the accurate reading of a code by a CD player or a store checkout all require the type of light produced by a laser. ☐

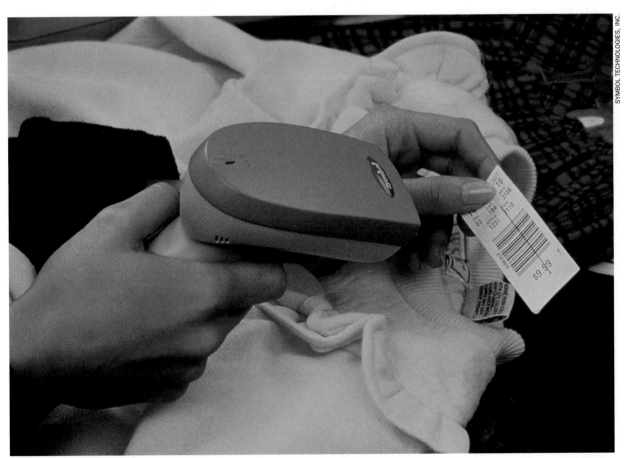

Lasers are used to read the bar codes on most of the things we buy.

LESSON 22
Combining Lenses

How does a telescope
work? Can you make one?

INTRODUCTION

A simple magnifier has only one lens. Do all optical devices that magnify objects have just one lens? Do microscopes or telescopes contain only one lens? If not, why do they contain more than one lens? How are these lenses selected, and how do they work together inside the device? In this lesson, you will investigate these questions as you select and use lenses to design and construct a simple telescope.

OBJECTIVES FOR THIS LESSON

Investigate a number of lenses and determine their type and approximate focal length.

Design and construct a simple telescope.

Discuss the role of the components of a telescope.

Getting Started

1. One member of your group should collect the plastic box of materials. Divide the materials between the pairs in your group. Each pair should have four different lenses.

2. Use your knowledge of lenses to determine the type and the approximate focal lengths of these lenses. Be prepared to share your conclusions with the class.

MATERIALS FOR LESSON 22

For you and your lab partner
4 lenses
1 meterstick
1 ball of clay
1 paper towel

Inquiry 22.1
Making a Simple Telescope

PROCEDURE

1. Can a simple telescope be made using some of the lenses you have been given? Experiment with the lenses and determine whether they can be combined in some way so that they magnify a distant object.

2. When you have the lenses arranged, determine how you could use only the lenses, clay, and the meterstick to build a simple telescope.

3. Construct your telescope. Adjust it to obtain the clearest enlarged image you can of the distant object your teacher identifies. In your science notebook, draw a labeled diagram of your telescope. Also provide information on the type, focal length, and position of each lens in your telescope.

4. Examine the telescope made by another pair of students. Compare their design with yours. Here are some points to consider:

Have they used the same order, position, and combination of lenses?

Does their telescope work as well as yours?

Can you improve on your design?

5. Explain the construction of your telescope to the class. Your explanation should include information on the order, position, and focal length of the lenses you used.

6. Your teacher will ask you to view another object, closer than the one you looked at first. Adjust your telescope so that you can see the object clearly. Be prepared to discuss the following questions with the class.

What adjustments did you have to make to get the object in focus?

How are these adjustments made using a commercially made telescope or a pair of binoculars?

REFLECTING ON WHAT YOU'VE DONE

1. In your notebook, draw a diagram of a cross-section of your telescope. Include in your diagram the light rays from a distant object entering the lens of the telescope and their approximate paths from one lens to the other and to the observer's eye.

2. Read "How Telescopes Work."

3. Check your telescope design. Does it suffer from chromatic aberrations? What causes these aberrations, and which telescope design avoids them?

4. Before returning the lenses to the plastic box, use the paper towel to wipe off any fingerprints.

How Telescopes Work

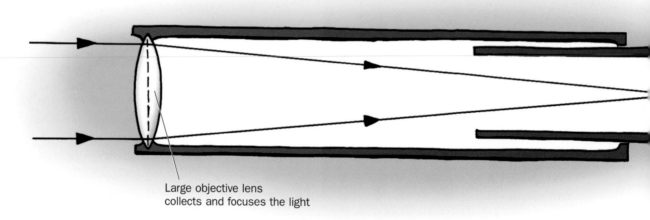

Large objective lens
collects and focuses the light

The components of a simple refracting telescope. This type of telescope is often referred to as a Keplerian telescope because it was used by the famous astronomer Johannes Kepler (1571–1630). Is the image produced by this telescope upright or inverted?

In 1608, a Dutch optician invented a device that altered our entire view of the universe. His name was Hans Lippershey (1570–1619). His invention arose from the simple observation that when two convex lenses were aligned at the correct distance from each other, they made distant objects look closer. By putting the lenses into a tube, Lippershey constructed what is believed to be the world's first telescope.

All telescopes collect electromagnetic radiation and focus it in some way. But not all telescopes are the same. Some, such as radio telescopes, do not use lenses at all. They don't collect visible light, but instead look for objects (for example, pulsars that emit radio waves) by using concave reflectors to focus invisible radio waves coming from the objects. Optical telescopes collect visible light. They come in two main forms: refracting telescopes, which use only lenses, and reflecting telescopes, which use mirrors and lenses.

Hans Lippershey's telescope was a refracting telescope. Refracting telescopes contain at least two lenses. The lens at one end of the tube of a refracting telescope collects light from a distant object. This lens is called the objective lens, and its job is to focus a real image of the object. The objective lens is usually large and has a long focal length. A second lens close to the eye—one with a shorter focal length—magnifies this real image. This lens is called the eyepiece. Lippershey's new invention was a boon to sailors and it spread rapidly along trade routes. Within a year of its invention, telescopes could be purchased in many parts of Europe. The telescope soon became popular with astronomers.

The Italian scientist Galileo (1564–1642) used the telescope to revolutionize astronomy. He modified Lippershey's earlier design by making the eyepiece a concave, rather than a convex, lens. One advantage of this design was

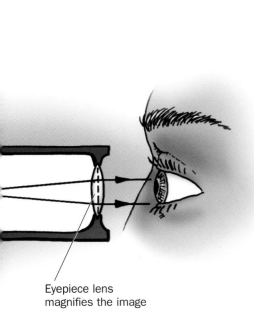

Eyepiece lens
magnifies the image

Isaac Newton made this
telescope. He has been
credited with the construction of the first reflecting
telescope. For this rea-
son, these telescopes are
sometimes called
Newtonian reflectors.

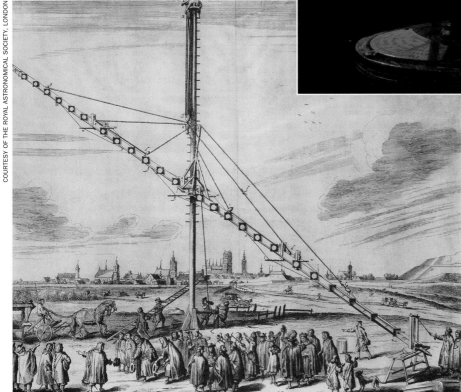

An early telescope being used for astronomical observation

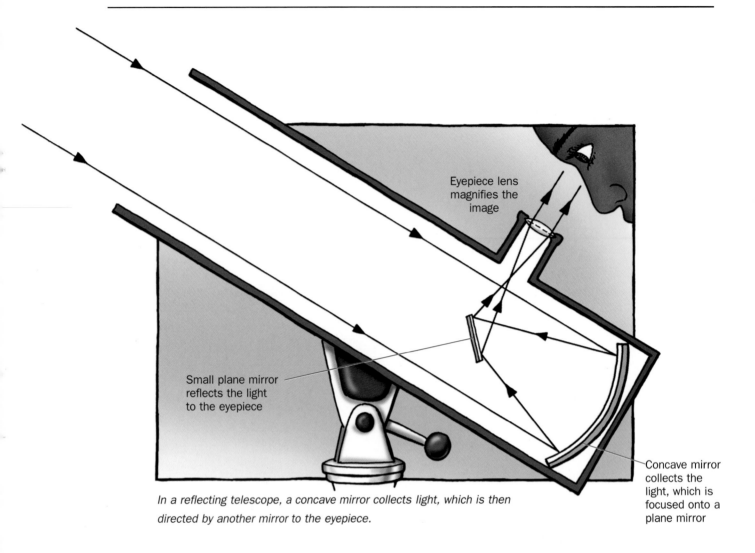

In a reflecting telescope, a concave mirror collects light, which is then directed by another mirror to the eyepiece.

Eyepiece lens magnifies the image

Small plane mirror reflects the light to the eyepiece

Concave mirror collects the light, which is focused onto a plane mirror

that the final image was right-side up! However, the area of sky that could be observed with a Galilean telescope was smaller than the area that could be observed with Lippershey's design. Most modern refracting telescopes are closer to Lippershey's design but contain combinations of lenses to make the image upright.

But there is a problem with refracting telescopes. Their lenses can produce chromatic aberrations—a colored blur around the image you read about in Lesson 18. Modern telescopes contain achromatic lenses that reduce chromatic aberration to a minimum. Early astronomers built reflecting telescopes that solved the problem in a different manner. They used mirrors instead of lenses. It was probably Isaac Newton

who built the first effective reflecting telescope. He followed a design suggested by Scottish astronomer James Gregory (1638–1675).

Light entering a reflecting telescope falls on a large concave mirror, usually at the bottom of a wide tube. The light is reflected onto another mirror, which diverts the image to an eyepiece on the side of the tube.

This basic design is still used, although sometimes the light is reflected back down through a hole in the mirror to an eyepiece. Because mirrors do not act as prisms, they don't split mixtures of different colored light and don't produce chromatic aberrations. Most big ground-based astronomical telescopes are reflecting telescopes. The Hubble Space Telescope you read about in Lesson 16 is also a reflecting telescope. ❑

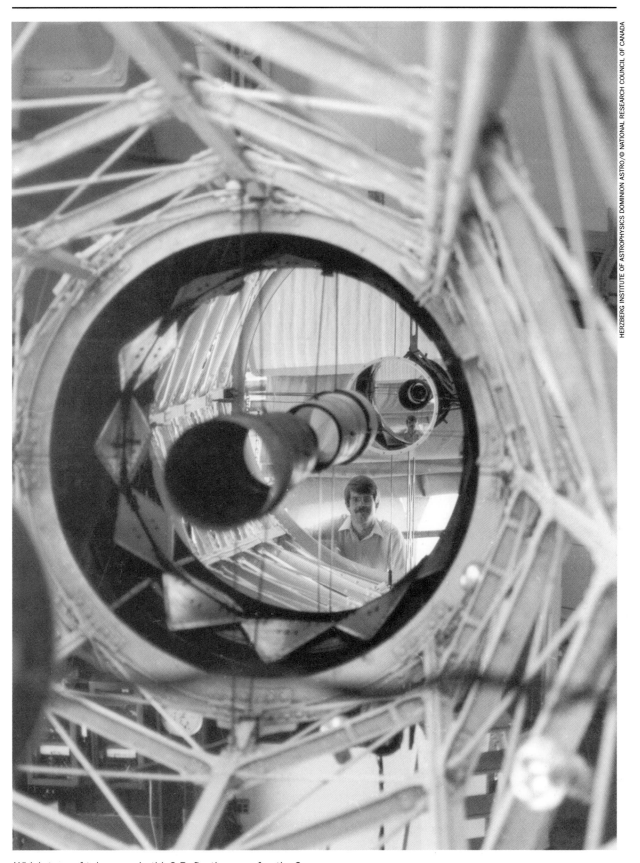

Which type of telescope is this? Reflecting or refracting?

Dissecting a Camera

JEFF MCADAMS, PHOTOGRAPHER, COURTESY OF CAROLINA BIOLOGICAL SUPPLY COMPANY

How is a photograph made and what role does the camera play in the process?

INTRODUCTION

Do you own a camera? What type of camera is it? Do you know how it works? What is inside this optical device? Regardless of type or manufacturer, all cameras have certain features in common. In this lesson, you will investigate how a camera works by dissecting a disposable camera.

OBJECTIVES FOR THIS LESSON

Identify the components of a camera.

Identify the function of each camera component.

Discuss the process of taking a photograph.

Getting Started

MATERIALS FOR LESSON 23

For you
1 pair of safety goggles

For you and your lab partner
1 small screwdriver
1 nonflash disposable camera
1 white screen
1 sheet of white paper

1. One member of your group should collect the plastic box of materials. Divide the materials in the plastic box between the pairs in your group.

2. Work with your partner to examine the outside of the camera. Draw a sketch in your science notebook of the camera and label all the components you can identify.

3. Discuss with your partner what you think each component does.

4. Your teacher will lead a class discussion about these camera components and their possible functions.

Inquiry 23.1
Dissecting a Disposable Camera

PROCEDURE

1. Use the questions below to help you make observations. Discuss the questions and your observations with other students. As you make observations, record them in your science notebook.

2. The exact construction of your camera will depend on its make and model. However, most disposable cameras have the same basic construction. Open the small door on the end of the camera. Inside is a chamber that sits below the film winder. This film compartment used to contain the exposed film, but the film has been removed from the camera.

   Which way did the winder need to be turned to advance the film?

3. Examine the access to the film compartment.

   Why is the camera constructed so that light is excluded from the film compartment?

4. Try to avoid breaking the parts of the camera as you take it apart—you will be asked to try to reassemble the camera after you have taken it apart. Place parts you remove on the sheet of white paper (see Figure 23.1). Be careful not to lose any of them—you'll need them later. Carefully remove the front of the camera and then the back of the camera. Try not to crack the casing or damage the interior of the camera. Watch out for parts that may fall out of the camera.

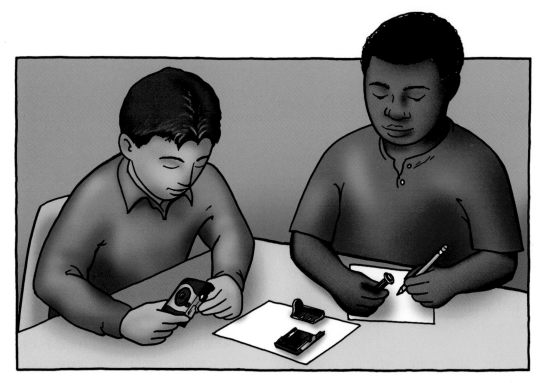

Figure 23.1 *Carefully take the camera apart. (Use the questions as a guide to help you make observations as you do so.) Place the parts you remove onto the white paper. Make notes in your notebook as you go.*

What color is the inside of the camera? Why?

5. Try to trace the path the film takes as it runs through the camera.

What is the function of the various compartments, gears, and wheels?

6. The film that was in the camera had sprocket holes along its edge. (See the illustration in the reader "Recording a Picture.")

Would advancing the film move any other components within the camera? If so, what is the purpose of this mechanism?

7. Locate the shutter. Find out how to prime the shutter. After priming the shutter, shade the back of the camera with your hand and depress the shutter release.

What do you need to do to make the shutter work?

What did you observe when you pressed the shutter release?

What did you notice about the speed at which the shutter opens and closes? Why is such a speed necessary?

Can you vary the speed of the shutter on this camera? Why would you want to?

8. Examine and then remove the viewfinder.

   What effect does the viewfinder have on light?

   Does the viewfinder contain any lenses? If so, how many and what types?

   Why are these types of lenses used in the viewfinder?

9. Remove the winding mechanism. Try to reassemble it and determine the function of each of its components. Try to get it to work again.

10. Use the winding mechanism to open and close the shutter.

   What makes the shutter close so quickly?

   Can you get the shutter to stay open? If you can, try looking from the inside of the camera out through the lens.

   Can you focus on the objects at which the camera is pointing?

11. Carefully pull off the lens. Try not to damage it. What type of lens is it? Look through the lens first at the print on this page and then at distant objects. Try to get the lens to form an image on the white screen.

   Can you determine the lens's approximate focal length?

   Does this camera have adjustable focusing?

12. Reexamine the shutter mechanism and look at the hole behind the lens. This is called the aperture. Think back to the pinhole camera you constructed.

   Why do you think such a small aperture was chosen for this camera?

13. Here is the ultimate challenge! Reassemble the camera. Can you get it working again?

REFLECTING ON WHAT YOU'VE DONE

1. Your teacher will lead a discussion on the results of your dissection. Be prepared to contribute your observations and ideas.

2. In your notebook, draw a cross-section (cut through the center) of the camera from front to back. Label each component and write a short description of its function directly under its label.

Recording a Picture

There are two main ways to record pictures—
using film or capturing images electronically.

How Film Works

Photographic film can be black and
white or color. Black-and-white film
records different levels of light intensity. Color film records the intensity
of different colors of light. Color film
is the most widely used type of film. A
color film is made of three layers.

One layer is sensitive to blue light,
another to green light, and a third layer to
red light. When the film is exposed for a fraction of second, each layer detects and records
the amount of each of these colors in the image.

Processing color film to make photographs takes
place in two main stages: developing and printing. In
the first stage, the film is developed. It is treated so that
dyes attach to the film where it has been exposed to
light. These dyes produce the strange colors you see on
the pieces of film you get back from the film processor.
These pieces of film are called negatives and are used in the
printing process. In the second stage of the process, light is
shone through these negatives and the image recorded on them

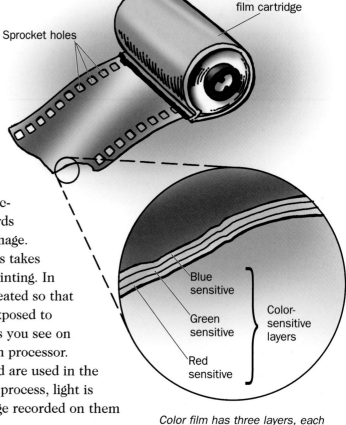

Color film has three layers, each
of which is sensitive to a different
color of light.

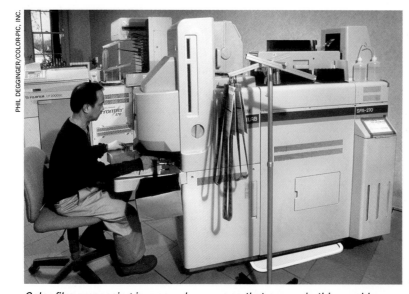

Color film processing is a complex process that occurs in this machine.

To make color prints, a negative image (left) is made in film. The negative image is used to make a positive image (right) on photographic paper. How do you think slide or movie film differs from the film used to make color prints?

is projected onto special light-sensitive paper. The image on the paper is usually larger than the negative and is therefore referred to as an enlargement. Like film, the light-sensitive paper has three color layers and is developed in similar dyes. The negative colors are turned back into positive ones on the paper—the same as the original image that was photographed.

Digital Photography

Today, many people use digital cameras to capture images. Digital cameras do not contain film. In place of the film, most digital cameras contain a device called a charge-coupled device (CCD). The CCDs in cameras are arrays, usually of millions of tiny light-sensitive diodes. When light strikes these diodes, electrical energy is produced. The amount of light striking each diode determines the amount of electrical energy produced. (The more light that strikes the diodes, the more energy is produced.) A microscopic red, green, or blue filter over different diodes spread throughout the array determines which color the diode is sensitive to. When a picture is taken, the electrical signals from the CCD are converted into digital signals. These are sent to a microprocessor that uses software to convert the signals into a picture. The picture can be shown on a screen, stored in digital form on a memory chip or disk, or printed onto paper. □

Digital cameras are becoming increasingly popular. Will they completely replace cameras that use film?

MAKING PICTURES WITH LIGHT
A Timeline for Some Important Events in the Development of Photography

Photography started about 200 years ago. It developed very rapidly. Most of the major advances in the development of photographic techniques took place in the first 100 years. Use this timeline to discover when different developments took place. Think about the impact these have had on your life and the lives of your ancestors.

PHOTOGRAPHIC HISTORY COLLECTION, NATIONAL MUSEUM OF AMERICAN HISTORY, SMITHSONIAN INSTITUTION NEG. 2001-9184

William Fox Talbot develops the first system using photographic negatives.

1816 Joseph Niepces uses a photosensitive chemical to record an image on light-sensitive paper.

1835 The first photographic negative is made by William Fox Talbot.

1839 The first photographic camera is marketed. It is bulky and takes daguerreotypes.

1851 The first electric flash is used in photography.

1879 George Eastman invents a mass-production process for photographic plates on glass.

1888 The first camera preloaded with film is marketed. The camera is shipped backed to its manufacturer, Kodak, for film processing.

1894 The Lumier brothers, working in France, invent the Cinematographique—a combination movie camera and projector.

1800 — 1850

1822 One of the earliest surviving photographs (taken by Neipces) is made.

1837 Louis Jacques Daguerre makes a photograph on a copper plate treated with light-sensitive silver. This process becomes the first practical method of photography. These photographs are called daguerreotypes.

1848 Glass plates, covered in photosensitive jelly, are used to make negatives.

1861 The first hand-held miniature camera is sold.

1882 The first photographic film is invented.

1892 The first method of color photography is invented.

GERNSHEIM COLLECTION, HARRY RANSOM HUMANITIES RESEARCH CENTER, THE UNIVERSITY OF TEXAS AT AUSTIN

An early photograph by Niepces

LIBRARY OF CONGRESS, PRINTS & PHOTOGRAPHS DIVISION, LC-USZ6-2064

A daguerreotype of Abraham Lincoln

The Brownie was the first popular camera made in large numbers.

This Tarzan movie was one the earliest "talkies." It came out in 1929. Is the gorilla real?

1900 The first mass-marketed camera, the Kodak Brownie, is sold. Its price is $1.00.

1908 Color photography becomes available but is very expensive.

1926 Movies with sound are developed and start to become popular.

1939 The first color movie—a short cartoon by filmmaker Walt Disney—is shown.

1963 Polaroid introduces instant color film.

1978 The first point-and-shoot auto focus camera is introduced.

2000 Digital still cameras become more popular. Digital cameras become cheaper and produce better pictures. Some record short movies and sound.

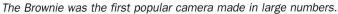

1900   **1950**   **2000**

1895 The first public screening of a motion picture takes place. The movie, and those that follow, have no sound (silent movies).

1905 Silent cinema becomes increasingly popular.

1914 The first 35-mm camera—still a standard for photographers—is developed. (35 mm refers to the size of the film.)

1935 The first commercially available color-slide film, developed for Kodak by Leopold Gadowsky and Leopold Manners, is marketed.

1942 Modern color print film becomes available.

1970 IMAX® movies are introduced.

1987 The first digital still camera goes on the market.

George Eastman, the founder of what became the Eastman Kodak Company, is considered the founding father of popular photography.

MATHEW BRADY
RECORDER OF HISTORY

PHOTOGRAPHIC HISTORY COLLECTION, NATIONAL MUSEUM OF AMERICAN HISTORY, SMITHSONIAN INSTITUTION NEG. 72-2740

Mathew Brady was one of America's greatest photographers. He pioneered new approaches to the art and science of photography.

Even as a teenager, Mathew Brady had many talents. A hard worker and good craftsman, he arrived in New York City in 1839 at the age of 16. Soon he started his own business making jewelry boxes for wealthy New Yorkers. Also interested in art, Mathew took lessons in painting; but his real passion was his hobby, daguerreotypy.

Daguerreotypy—then a new art form—was a process that used light to record images on metal plates. It was the forerunner of photography. Working with a friend who had learned the process in Europe, Mathew was soon an expert. In 1844, at the age of 21, he opened his own studio and gallery. His hobby had become his job. He began winning prizes for the high

quality of his work. Within a year he was exhibiting his pictures around the world. On his travels, he learned about even newer processes for making pictures. He quickly mastered and became an expert in these modern photographic methods. Using his talents as a photographer, Mathew Brady set out on a quest that occupied much of the rest of his life.

A Photographic Chronicle

"From the first, I regarded myself as under obligation to my country to preserve the faces of its historic men and mothers," said Mathew Brady, when asked about his passion for recording important historical figures. Mathew Brady started his career specializing in portraits. To

These two portraits were taken by Brady. The picture of General Sam Houston (left)—President and later Governor of Texas—is a daguerreotype. The picture of Ulysses S. Grant (right), Civil War General and later President of the United States, was taken using a later process involving light-sensitive glass plates.

pursue this passion, he opened a studio in Washington, D.C., and began taking portraits of the famous people of the day. Over the course of his career, he photographed hundreds of dignitaries, including 20 Presidents of the United States and countless other famous people including diplomats and members of the royalty.

By the 1860s, Brady was recognized as America's greatest portrait photographer. So people were shocked when in 1861, at the peak of his profession, he decided to take his career in a new direction. Mathew Brady decided to chronicle in photographs one of the pivotal events in our history—the Civil War.

Nobody had tried such a thing before. How would one make a photographic record of a war in the field? Brady knew it would be a big job. He put all his resources into the project, organizing a corps of photographers. Brady and his photographers went with soldiers into the field, often dodging bullets to get the photographs they wanted. Their photos, like the ones taken of battlefield corpses after the war's most bloody battles at Antietam and Gettysburg, brought the horrors of modern war home to the public.

Over the course of the war Brady built up a huge collection of photographs. He financed the

Photographing a war took a lot of equipment, and in those days none of it was small. Brady's photographers used wagons to transport their bulky materials.

NATIONAL ARCHIVES AND RECORDS ADMINISTRATION

whole enterprise with his own money. After the war, he published these photographs in book form. But by that time people were war weary. Many were sick of the horror shown in Brady's photographs.

Brady's books of war photos did not sell well and his money had run out. Brady declared bankruptcy and lost all his property. Of his photographs he said, "No one will ever know what they cost me; some of them almost cost me my life."

Mathew Brady, America's first great photographer and photojournalist, died in 1896. He was so poor that his friends in the art world had to pay for part of his funeral. Like so many great artists, Mathew Brady's photographs are appreciated more now than they were during his lifetime. ☐

Brady's corps of photographers recorded the horrors rather than the glories of war. This 1863 photograph shows the battlefield after Gettysburg.

24
Animal Optics

The eyes of this fictional superhero are rather special. Do your eyes emit or absorb light?

INTRODUCTION

How do animals see? Eyes—the sense organ responsible for sight—come in a wide variety of forms. How do they work? How do they detect light or images and what happens to the information they gather? You will start this lesson by examining the eyes of the animal with which you are most familiar—you. You will investigate and look at a model of the human eye before reading about how your eye works. You will look at how the eye and brain receive and interpret the information and will discover that sometimes you can't always believe your eyes! You will discuss the eyes of other animals—how and why they differ from our own. You may find that eyes have some things in common with other optical devices you have investigated or read about.

OBJECTIVES FOR THIS LESSON

Examine the human eye.

Relate the structure of the eye to its function as an optical device.

Compare human optics to the optics of a camera.

Discuss how the eyes and brain work together as a visual system.

Experience and discuss optical illusions.

Look at and discuss the nature of the eyes of other animals.

Getting Started

1. Imagine you have to design a working eye for a robot. Discuss with your group what the eye would have to be able to do.

2. Now think about the design of your robot's eye. (You may find it useful to draw a sketch.) Look back to the camera in Lesson 23. This may give you a few ideas.

What would it need to perform these functions?

3. In your notebook, jot down notes of your group's ideas. Be prepared to share them with the class.

MATERIALS FOR LESSON 24

For you
1 copy of Student Sheet 24.1: Investigating Human Eyes
1 copy of Student Sheet 24.2: Why Do You Have Two Eyes in the Front of Your Head?

For you and your lab partner
1 flashlight
2 D-cell batteries
1 large mirror
1 thick convex lens
1 thin convex lens
1 cardboard tube

Inquiry 24.1
Investigating Human Eyes

PROCEDURE

1. One member of your group should collect the plastic box of materials. Divide the materials between the pairs in your group.

2. Look at your eye in the mirror.

A. Draw an accurate picture of your eye on Student Sheet 24.1: Investigating Human Eyes.

3. In dim light, look at your eye in the mirror. Shine a flashlight into your eye.

B. Record what you observe when you shine the flashlight into your eye.

4. Now examine Figure 24.1 and the model of the eye your teacher has shown you.

C. Use the figure and model to help you label the parts of the eye you have drawn on your picture.

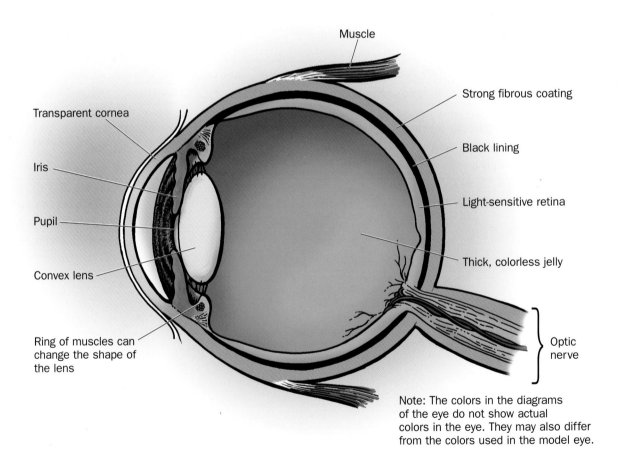

Muscle

Strong fibrous coating

Black lining

Transparent cornea

Light-sensitive retina

Iris

Pupil

Thick, colorless jelly

Convex lens

Optic nerve

Ring of muscles can change the shape of the lens

Note: The colors in the diagrams of the eye do not show actual colors in the eye. They may also differ from the colors used in the model eye.

Figure 24.1 *Use this picture and the model of the eye to identify the parts of the eye.*

5. Discuss with your partner your observations of your own eyes, the model, and Figure 24.1.

D. Use the results of your discussion and your knowledge of light, lenses, and optical devices (particularly the camera) to predict which part(s) of the eye performs the following function(s). Record your predictions in Table 1 on Student Sheet 24.1.

- Allows light into the eye
- Controls the amount of light entering the eye
- Focuses light
- Detects light
- Prevents reflection inside the eye
- Transfers information from the eye to the brain

6. Discuss the following questions with your group. Be prepared to share your observations and ideas with the class.

How does the human eye compare with your ideas for a robot eye?

How does the human eye compare with the design of the camera you dissected in Lesson 23?

7. Look through the lenses you have been given.

E. Describe the lenses. How do the shapes of these lenses compare with the lens in the eye?

F. Each eye has one lens. What shape would the lens in the eye have to be if it could focus on distant objects? What shape would it have to be if it could focus on near objects? Draw the shapes.

G. Unlike these rigid plastic lenses, the lens in the eye is flexible. How could the flexible nature of the lens in the eye help the eye to focus on near and distant objects?

8. Read "How the Eye Produces a Clear Image."

HOW THE EYE PRODUCES A CLEAR IMAGE

Light rays from objects we observe enter the eye. These rays are refracted at each place they travel from one transparent substance to another. Most of this refraction takes place as the light enters the eye at the cornea—the transparent outer covering of the eye. The light is also refracted as it goes from the jelly inside the eye into the lens and back into the jelly again. The lens adjusts its shape so that these refracted rays are brought into focus on the retina—a layer of light-sensitive cells at the back of the eye. As you can see from the illustration, the image is upside down. Tiny nerves connected to the light-sensitive cells of the retina carry signals along a larger optic nerve to the brain.

How the Lens Puts Things Into Focus

The lens of the eye is a flexible convex lens. The lens can change shape—it can become thicker or thinner. Ligaments (small fibers) are fixed to the rim of the lens. The other ends of the ligaments are attached to a ring of muscle that surrounds the lens. The eye uses this muscle to change the shape of the lens depending on whether it wants to look at near or far objects. When this ring of muscle is relaxed it becomes wider and the ligaments

The eye is a complex and delicate organ. You should have your eyes checked regularly.

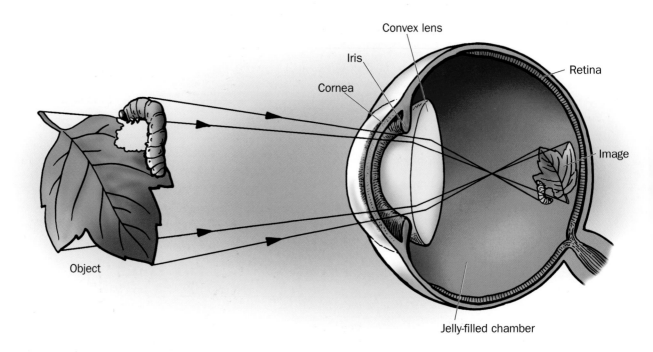

Light is refracted at each surface—as it enters the cornea, the lens, and the jelly inside the eye. The lens adjusts its shape to focus the image on the retina. The image is inverted, but the brain interprets it as being right-side up.

pull the lens into a flatter, thinner shape. In this shape the lens has a long focal length and focuses on distant objects.

When the eye looks at near objects, the ring of muscle contracts. The ligaments attached to the lens become loose, and the lens springs back to its thick, rounder shape. When the lens is this shape, it has a shorter focal length and focuses on near objects. The ability of the eye to adjust the focal length of the lens enables the eye to focus on distant, and then near, objects.

As people get older, the lenses in their eyes often become less flexible and do not spring back into shape. This makes close-up work—reading, for example—difficult. Many older people wear reading glasses or contact lenses to correct this change in their vision.

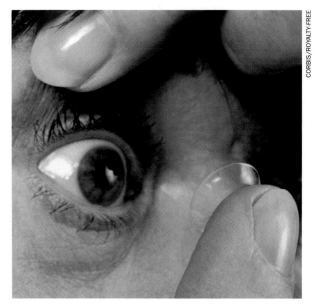

Eyes that have problems focusing can usually be corrected by contact lenses or glasses.

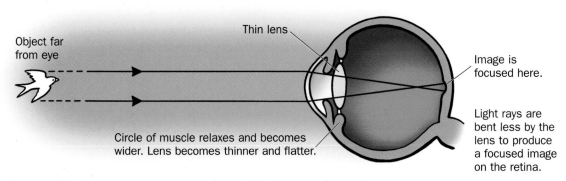

Object far from eye

Thin lens

Image is focused here.

Light rays are bent less by the lens to produce a focused image on the retina.

Circle of muscle relaxes and becomes wider. Lens becomes thinner and flatter.

When the ring of muscle that surrounds the lens is wide, ligaments fixed to the lens pull the lens into a flat shape. The lens has a longer focal length. This shape of lens focuses more distant objects onto the back of the eye.

When the muscles around the lens contract, the lens returns to its thick, rounder shape. Its focal length is shorter, and the eye can focus near objects onto the back of the eye.

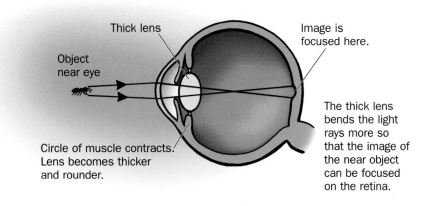

Thick lens

Image is focused here.

Object near eye

Circle of muscle contracts. Lens becomes thicker and rounder.

The thick lens bends the light rays more so that the image of the near object can be focused on the retina.

Inquiry 24.2
Why Do You Have Two Eyes in the Front of Your Head?

PROCEDURE

1. What would it be like if you had only one eye? Try looking at things with one eye. What difference, if any, does it make? Discuss your ideas with your partner.

2. Hold a pen or pencil in a vertical position at arm's length. Look at it with both eyes. Then close one eye. Now open the other eye and close the one you had open. Do this a few times and then respond to A and B on Student Sheet 24.2: Why Do You Have Two Eyes in the Front of Your Head?

   A. What does the pen or pencil appear to do when you alternately open and close each of your eyes?

   B. What does this tell you about the image you get from each eye?

3. Get a pen or marker with a removable top. Hold the pen at arm's length in one hand and the top in the other. Starting each time with your hand holding the top near your body quickly put the top on and off the pen 10 times. Now close one eye and repeat the procedure again (see Figure 24.2).

   C. Record data comparing your attempts at replacing the top with two eyes open with your attempts with one eye open.

   D. What can you conclude from your data? Suggest one reason why you have two eyes. What role do you think the brain plays in this process?

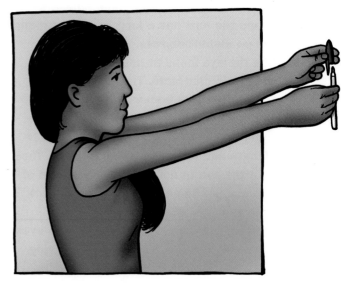

Figure 24.2   *Hold the pen in a vertical position in one hand. Starting with your hand holding the top near your body, try to quickly put the top on and take it off the pen 10 times. First keep both eyes open and then try it again with one eye closed.*

4. Discuss E and F with your group before answering them on the student sheet.

   E. Would two eyes perform this function as well if they were in opposite sides of your head (like a chicken)? Give reasons for your answer.

   F. Why do you think some predators (like cats or owls) often have eyes facing forward, but prey species (like mice or pigeons) often have eyes in opposite sides of their heads?

5. Think back to Lesson 1, Inquiry 1.7. Do you remember when you looked down a tube? If not, use the tube to repeat the experiment.

   Can you now explain your observations?

6. Read "Optical Illusions."

OPTICAL ILLUSIONS

When you looked down the tube in Inquiry 1.7 you experienced an optical illusion. Optical illusions occur when your eyes and brain fail to gather visual information or misinterpret the visual information they do gather. Some optical illusions result from the way your eyes work. Other optical illusions result from your brain incorrectly interpreting the information that your eyes provide. Over millions of years, our eyes and brains have evolved mechanisms to provide us with accurate and useful information about our surroundings. But sometimes these mechanisms do not work as well as expected, and then you can't believe your eyes!

Inquiry 24.3
Experiencing Some Optical Illusions

PROCEDURE

1. Look at the cross and the dot in Figure 24.3.

2. Hold the page with the cross and dot at arm's length. Close your left eye and stare at the cross with your right eye. The cross should still be visible.

3. Bring the paper slowly toward your face.

   What do you observe?

   Was your sense of sight tricked? If so, how?

Figure 24.3 *Look at the cross and the dot and carefully follow the procedure in Steps 2 and 3.*

4. Look at Figure 24.4. On the diagram, you will see that the eye has a point where the optic nerve leaves the retina. At this spot, there are no light-sensitive cells.

Would you be able to detect light that entered the eye and fell on this spot?

How could this information be relevant to the observations you have just made?

5. Sometimes optical illusions are the result of how your eyes work. At other times, they are the result of your brain incorrectly interpreting the information supplied by the eyes.

Which of these two types of illusions is the one you have just experienced?

6. Look at the examples of optical illusions shown in Figures 24.5.

7. With your partner, carefully examine each illusion. In some cases, you may wish to use a ruler to check what you think you observe. Discuss how you think each illusion tricks your eyes or your brain.

8. Think about the following questions. Be prepared to share your observations and ideas with the class.

What do these illusions tell you about the way the brain interprets information from your eyes?

Why is it important to make measurements when conducting a scientific investigation?

How reliable is eyewitness testimony?

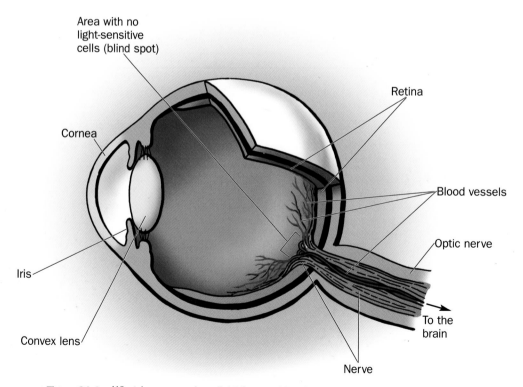

Figure 24.4 *What happens when light focused by the eye falls on an area where there are no light-sensitive cells?*

Start with illusion A. Stare at the flag for 10 seconds, then close your eyes. What do you see?

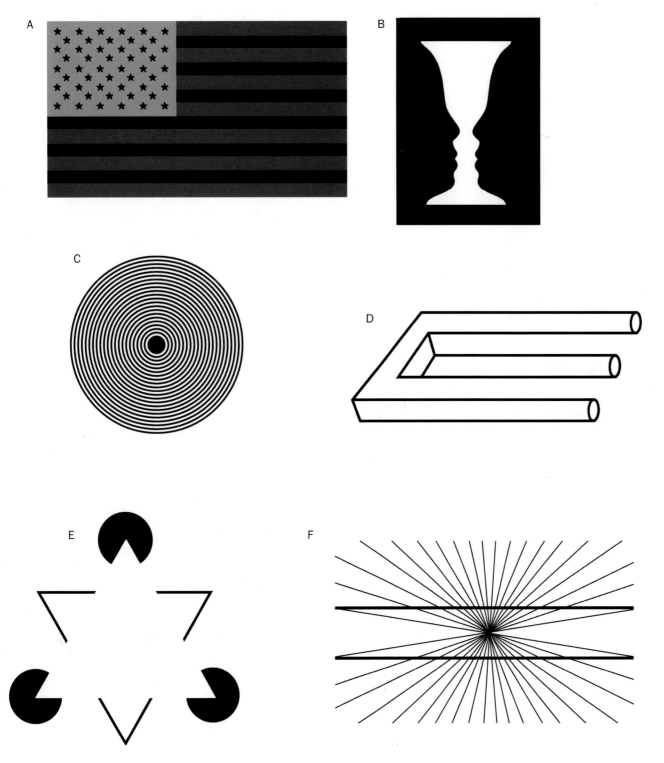

Figure 24.5 *Examine these optical illusions. How do they trick your eyes and brain?*

REFLECTING ON WHAT YOU'VE DONE

1. Read "How Do You Detect Light?" Be prepared to contribute to a class discussion about the reader.

2. Your teacher will show you a video about sight. After watching the video, try to imagine what it would be like to have different numbers of eyes, eyes on different parts of your body, or different types of eyes. Look at the photographs of different animal eyes. Speculate how the view these animals have of the world may differ from your own. Discuss with your group how the type, number, and the position of animal eyes (including human eyes) affects an animal's sense of sight.

Horses cannot see in full color. The position of their eyes tells you something about their field of vision.

No, this is not an alien. It's a tarsier. Why does it have big eyes that point forward?

How many eyes does a spider have? Imagine what it sees.

A cat has a reflective layer in its eye. Why is this adaptation important?

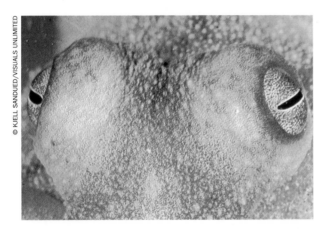

The octopus has excellent color vision. What is its field of vision like?

Why do chameleons have such strange eyes? How can they change their field of vision?

How do eyes on stalks allow this fiddler crab to increase its field of vision? Why would they be handy if you lived in a hole?

Insects have two big eyes (only one is shown here), each made up from lots of small simple eyes. Imagine what it would look like to peer through these compound eyes.

HOW DO YOU DETECT LIGHT?

How do your eyes detect light? You have seen how the cornea and the lens focus light on the retina. What happens next? The retina is made up of cells—about 130 million of them in each eye—that are sensitive to light. These cells contain pigments that change when light falls on them. These changes stimulate nerves that are attached to these cells. The stimulated nerves carry a signal to the brain. The brain interprets the signal—a process called visual perception.

There are two types of light-sensitive cells in the retina. One type of these cells, called rods, detects only light and dark—that is, shades of gray. These cells function in both bright and dim light. The other type, called cones, allow for color vision. They work only in quite bright light. Understanding the role of rods and cones explains why you may be able to see in a very dimly lit room but you can't see in color.

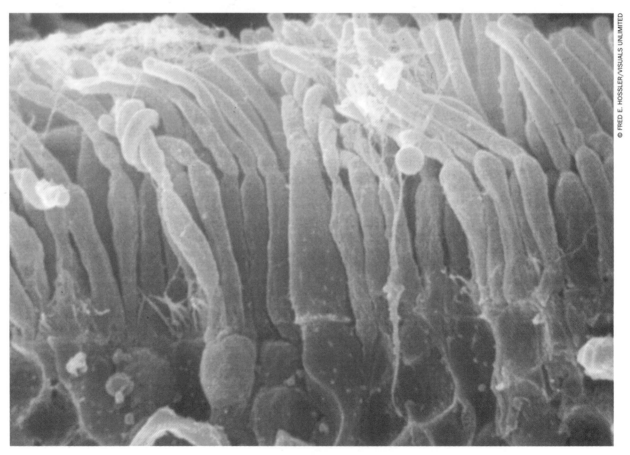

© FRED E. HOSSLER/VISUALS UNLIMITED

Light-sensitive cells in the retina are named according to their shape. The long thin cells are called rods and the cone-shaped cells are called cones. Only cones are involved in detecting color.

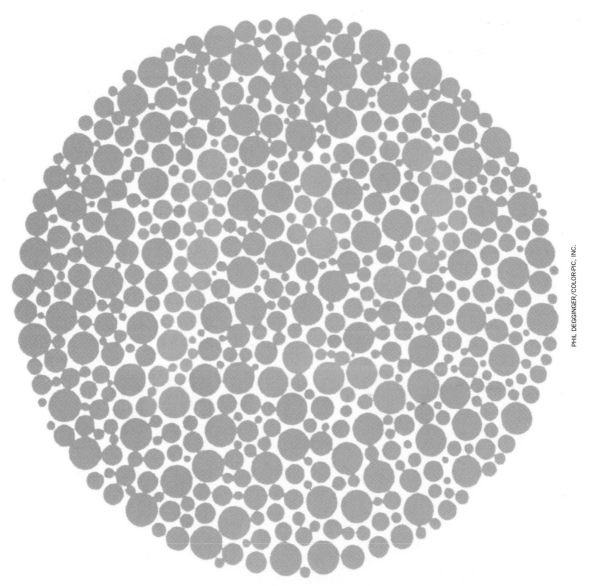

PHIL DEGGINGER/COLOR-PIC, INC.

Color-blind people have one or more types of cones missing from their retina. This image can be used to help diagnose red-green color blindness. What do you see when you look at this image? Can you read the number?

Three different types of cones respond to different wavelengths of light. The combination of these responses is interpreted by the brain as color. Remember that color is not a physical property of light. Rather, it is a sensation produced by the brain as it receives information from the cones in the retina. This is why you see, for example, a mixture of green and red light wavelengths as yellow. Your brain perceives this mixture of wavelengths as yellow—your eyes are not receiving any yellow wavelengths from the mixture.

If one type of cone is missing from a person's eyes, the person perceives color differently. This is referred to as color blindness. There are different types of color blindness. The most common form makes it hard for people to see the difference between red and green. Red-green color blindness is genetic and is very common among men. Probably one or two boys in your class are red-green color blind. Different types and degrees of color blindness can be diagnosed using special test cards. ☐

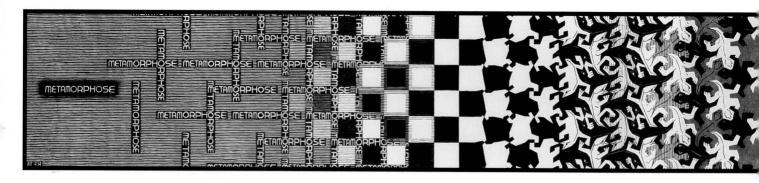

The IMPOSSIBLE WORLDS of M.C. ESCHER

Hand With Reflecting Sphere *is a self-portrait by the graphic artist M.C. Escher (1898–1972). Escher used reflection, patterns, and "impossible figures" to create works of art that confuse the human visual system.*

In most subjects, Maurits Cornelis Escher was not a very successful student. But he did have a gift for art; he lived for his art lessons. Escher went to an art school in Haarlem, in the Netherlands, where he trained in the graphic arts—drawing, painting, and printing. He particularly enjoyed making prints, a technique he used often in his later work.

Like many young graduates, when Escher completed art school he decided to travel. He was attracted to the warmer climate of southern Europe around the Mediterranean. He spent some time in Italy and made money sketching landscapes. He also went to Spain where he visited the Alhambra palace. This maze of buildings—a wonder of Arab architecture—stands on a hill overlooking the ancient city of Granada. Arab artists had decorated the walls of the palace with tiles arranged in repeating patterns. The mathematical name for the type of pattern they had used is tessella-

tion. These tessellated patterns captivated Escher. He found their geometry fascinating and began using similar patterns in his work. This was the beginning of Escher's life-long interest in the relationship between mathematics and art.

Escher produced many tessellation-like patterns in which repeated regular and irregular shapes interlock. One of his favorite approaches was to make prints, in which these patterns change, or metamorphose, slowly as they move across the print. For example, what starts out as a regular shape becomes distorted and changes into an insect; then perhaps a fish that may eventually evolve into a building. Look at the print spread across the top of this reader. Where do the shapes change to become different recognizable objects? Where do you first recognize the insect or the fish? Escher's art is playing tricks with how your visual system recognizes objects.

Escher began to experiment with other ways of confusing the eyes and brain. He became very interested in making impossible figures. These are drawings that trick the visual system into seeing impossible or changing images.

Most impossible figures rely on the brain's tendency to construct three-dimensional objects from flat, two-dimensional images—something we do all the time when we look at photographs or watch films. Look at his print *Convex and Concave*. Does the building change as you look at it? Do floors become ceilings or parts of the outside become inside? Escher's work confuses the viewer. It can make you think that water can flow uphill or that stairs can be linked in a continuous circular uphill stairway.

Escher developed his childhood gift for art, blended it with mathematics, and used both to create worlds of strange symmetry and illusion. He died in 1972 but left us impossible worlds of illusion—worlds that exploit the human visual system and will exist forever in his art. ☐

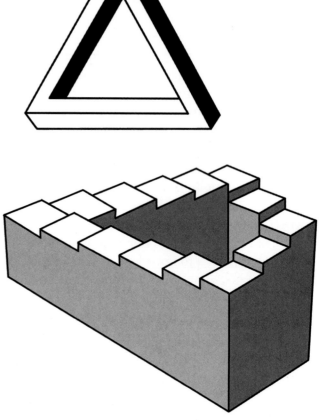

Two simple examples of impossible figures known as "strange loops": How do they trick the brain into observing the impossible? Escher used illusions like these in his art.

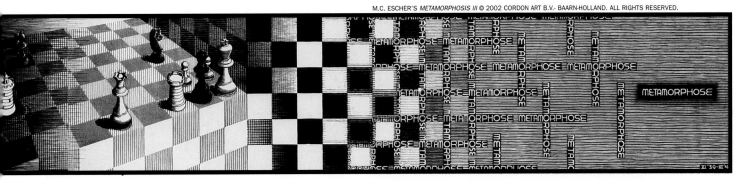

This is part of a 6-meter long print Escher produced called Metamorphosis III. *The tile-like objects and animals in the patterns transform effortlessly into each other. Is it difficult to decide where one object forms and another disappears?*

In his print Convex and Concave, *Escher uses optical illusions to confuse the viewer. The longer you look at this print, the more confusing it becomes.*

25

Communicating With Light

Light is the fastest way of sending information from one place to another. This lighthouse warns sailors that they are near dangerous waters. The flashing light provides information about the identity of the lighthouse.

© DAVID S. ADDISON/VISUALS UNLIMITED

INTRODUCTION

Your ability to detect light allows you to gather a lot of information about the surrounding environment. Think about all the kinds of information you receive by detecting light. Light also can be used to send specific information from one place to another. Because nothing travels faster than the speed of light, light provides the fastest means of communication. In this lesson, you will investigate some ways in which light can be used to send information.

OBJECTIVES FOR THIS LESSON

Explore how light can be used for communication.

Observe how light can be directed through transparent materials.

Investigate optical fibers and how they can be used in communication.

Observe and discuss total internal reflection.

Getting Started

1. We use our voices to speak to each other and transfer information. Voice communication uses sound waves. Discuss this question with your group:

How do we use light to transfer information?

2. Make a list of all the ways that light can be used to transfer information. Be prepared to discuss your examples with the class.

MATERIALS FOR LESSON 25

For you
1 copy of Student Sheet 25.3: Assessment Review—Part 3
1 copy of Student Sheet 25.4: Sample Assessment Questions for Part 3

For you and your lab partner
1 flashlight
2 D-cell batteries
1 length of black optical fiber
1 hand lens
1 red filter
1 green filter
1 blue filter

For your group
1 wooden block
Masking tape

Inquiry 25.1
Investigating an Optical Fiber

PROCEDURE

1. One member of your group should collect the plastic box of materials. Divide the materials between the pairs in your group. Record your responses for this inquiry in your science notebook.

2. Examine the black optical fiber. Discuss with your partner how it is constructed.

A. Draw a simple diagram of the fiber construction.

3. Can this fiber transmit light? Devise and conduct an investigation to answer this question.

B. Write a short paragraph describing what you did and what you discovered.

C. What evidence do you have that the optical fiber transmits a wide range of different wavelengths of light?

D. What do you notice about light where it comes out of the bare end of the optical fiber? Suggest an explanation for your observations.

4. Working with another pair, determine whether you can connect two pieces of fiber together so that the double-length piece transmits light.

E. If the joined lengths of optical fiber can transmit light, what measures did you have to take to ensure light transmission?

F. Is there any difference in the brightness of the beam when using the double-length fiber as compared to the single length of fiber? Can you suggest a reason for your result?

5. Your teacher will use a light pipe and a small laser to model how light can travel along a fiber.

G. Draw a diagram illustrating what you observe.

H. Where have you observed this type of reflection before?

Inquiry 25.2
Sending a Message Along an Optical Fiber

PROCEDURE

1. Work with your group. Discuss ways you can use the materials in the box to use light to transfer a simple message along a length of optical fiber. Think about the following question:

What would both the transmitter and receiver of the message need to know in order to successfully transfer information?

2. Devise a code that you can transmit along the optical fiber that could be used to instruct a member of your group to move the wooden block to an exact spot on a table somewhere in the room.

What sort of instructions will you have to give to your team members?

How will you represent these instructions?

3. Develop and test your ideas. Be prepared to describe and demonstrate them to the class.

4. What problems would your system of light communication have communicating over large distances? How could this problem be overcome? Think about the following questions. Be prepared to outline your ideas to the class.

Does your communication system have any other limitations?

How could these limitations be overcome?

REFLECTING ON WHAT YOU'VE DONE
Respond to the following questions in your notebook:

A. In Inquiry 25.2, you used a code to communicate with light. How could many different wavelengths of light be used to increase the amount of information that could be carried by a light communication device at any one time?

B. On-off signals—that is, binary (digital) code—are used to transmit information. Why is this type of code ideal for transmitting information along optical fibers?

Light Messages

The Great Wall of China was first built around 200 B.C. and has been altered many times since to protect the borders of the Chinese Empire. Its sentries used light to send urgent messages. Fires lit on guardhouses signaled an attack.

Sentry duty on the Great Wall of China was a lonely job. During that winter night in 210 B.C. bitter winds from the heart of Asia whipped across the top of the wall. Most of the sentries hid in the guardhouses. Huddled around fires, they exchanged tales of glorious battles fought long ago.

It was Xu Zhihong's turn to be out guarding this section of the wall. Above the whistling wind, he heard a clink of metal on stone. Peering over the parapet, he could just make out the glint of a sword in the moonlight. The wall and the Chinese Empire were being attacked. The whoosh of arrows joined the howl of the wind as he ran back to the guardhouse.

"The Huns are attacking!" he shouted. Xu could hear their footsteps behind him as he ran. Bursting through the door of the guardhouse, he knew he had only a few seconds left to live. "Light the Signal Fire," he cried.

Grabbing a lit torch, one of the guards scrambled up the steps to the roof of the guardhouse. Arrows fell around him as he plunged the torch into the heart of a stack of wood on the roof. As the attackers burst through the guardhouse door, the wood burst into flame. Within minutes, signal fires on guardhouses glowed along many kilometers of the Great Wall. Light from the fires signaled to the local garrison that the Chinese Empire was under attack. Another surprise attack by the Huns had been foiled.

An Inventive Flare

The Chinese also had great expertise in making fireworks. Martha Coston, an inventor from Philadelphia, adapted their ideas to make a light-signaling device. In 1871, she patented the "Pyrotechnic Night Signal." When fired in the air, this device produced a bright light visible from many kilometers away. These light-signaling devices became known as signal flares. They were widely used in the Civil War. They were later adopted worldwide, mainly as a device for ships to signal that they are in distress.

Martha Coston—Inventor of a light-signaling device that has saved the lives of many seafarers

Martha Coston's signal flares were widely used in the Civil War. Here the USS Rhode Island signals to another vessel for help with efforts to rescue the crew of the sinking USS Monitor.

In the days before telegraphs, telephones, and radios, light was widely used as a means of communication. At night, signal fires could be lit to signal an enemy attack; lamps of different colors could be used to communicate more complex messages. Messages could even be flashed using code. In daylight, flags and other signs could be used to communicate between watchtowers and ships. If these signals were made from high places, they could travel over many kilometers.

Signal towers were widely used before the days of telegraph. Various codes were used to transmit complex messages. Semaphore was one such code. It uses two flags to represent numbers and letters. Semaphore is still used today. By using several signal stations within sight of each other, messages could travel across an entire country or along the entire 5000-kilometer length of the Great Wall of China.

Morse code is one way in which flashes of light can be used to transmit complex messages. This code uses series of short and long flashes to represent letters and numbers. Powerful lamps with special shutters can be used to flash messages. Sometimes light from the Sun is harnessed for the same purpose and mirrors are used to flash sunlight over long distances. Special devices called heliographs were made for this purpose.

Even telephone messages could be carried by light. In 1880, Alexander Graham Bell invented the photophone, which used sunlight and a vibrating mirror to send voice messages along a beam of light.

But sending messages by light has its problems. What happens if it's a foggy or rainy day with poor visibility? How do you transmit the signal over very long distances? Building all those intermediate signal stations is expensive. What happens in very mountainous terrain or in big cities where the view may be blocked by hills or buildings? Eventually sending electrical signals along metal cables—as telegraph or telephone messages—or transmitting them using radio waves replaced messages using visible light.

Ships at sea still use flags to send signals. By using a telescope from the top of a mast, a sailor can read a flag message sent from many miles away. What message is this ship's captain sending?

The Fiber-Optic Revolution

Today, light plays a new role in communication. Light is used to send huge amounts of information long distances along cables. But these cables are not made from metal. They are made of glass.

Look through a window and you see the world outside. The view is bright and clear because the glass of the window transmits light. But what if the window were 500 meters thick? Would the view still be as clear? Would you be able to see anything through glass this thick? No, glass in a pane may look clear but if light had to pass through large amounts of window glass it would be absorbed.

So how do you get light to travel along kilometers of glass fiber-optic cable? There are two solutions. Design a super-transparent glass and use very intense light sources.

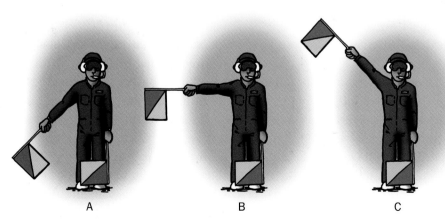

A B C

A sailor uses semaphore to signal another ship. Semaphore uses flags as a code to represent letters and numbers. Learn your ABCs in semaphore.

This heliograph used mirrors to reflect light from the Sun to signal messages over long distances. The user tapped out a message using a key check attached to the mirror. His partner looked for the return message.

In the search for a super-transparent glass, the trick was to make the glass as pure as possible. Beginning in the 1970s, really pure glass fibers were made. These super-transparent fibers of glass were improved over the next 10 years and can now carry a wide range of light wavelengths for long distances. The intense light source took the form of miniature lasers that work like the one in your CD player. Combining these two technologies allows fiber-optic cables to transmit signals over 60 kilometers. If the signals are automatically boosted at intervals, they can be transmitted any distance.

Fiber-optic cables carry messages all over the world. Each time you use a telephone you are probably using a fiber-optic cable. The electrical signal generated when you speak into the telephone is converted somewhere along the line into flashes of light. Fiber-optic cables even carry messages under the ocean to other continents. These large fiber-optic cables can contain hundreds of separate strands of optical fibers. They carry huge amounts of data—especially in digital form. This is why they form most of the network of cables that connect the computers that make up the Internet. When telephone conversations are converted into digital form, each strand can carry tens of thousands of phone messages at one time! Fiber-optic cables are more robust, cheaper, and more secure than old metal wire systems. Today, a different Xu Zhihong can sit at his desk in China and use light to communicate almost instantly to the other side of the world. ☐

Fiber-optic cables can contain many strands of optical fiber. Each fiber strand within the cable can carry thousands of channels of information—for example, different phone calls—each coded using a different wavelength of light.

26

End of Module Assessment: Bringing Some Ideas About Light Together

COURTESY OF DAVID MARSLAND/© NSRC

In the inquiry for this assessment you will be working with a partner. Discuss your observations and ideas with your partner, but record those that you individually think are correct.

INTRODUCTION

This lesson is designed to assess how much you have learned while working on the module *Light*. The assessment consists of two parts: a performance assessment (Inquiry 26.1) and a written assessment.

When doing the performance assessment, you will work with a partner. You may recognize objects from some inquiries you have already conducted. You may have already tried to explain some of the things you are going to observe. Carefully record what you observe. Points will be awarded for accurate observations and explanations. Think carefully about each part of the inquiry. Be sure to use your full knowledge about light when making your explanations.

OBJECTIVES FOR THIS LESSON

Use your knowledge of light and your inquiry skills to conduct an inquiry.

Use your knowledge of light to successfully complete a written assessment for the module *Light*.

Getting Started

1. Some students in the class will be conducting the performance assessment while others will do the written assessment.

2. When you take the performance assessment your teacher will assign you and your partner a set of materials. Make sure your set includes all the materials on the materials list.

3. You will need to discuss your observations and explanations with your partner but record only those that *you* consider correct. Do not share information or results with other pairs of students.

MATERIALS FOR LESSON 26

For you
- 1 copy of Student Sheet 26.1: Section A—Performance Assessment: Canned Light
- 1 copy of Student Sheet 26.2: Section B—Written Assessment Question Sheet
- 1 copy of Student Sheet 26.3: Section B—Written Assessment Answer Sheet

For you and your lab partner
- 1 flashlight
- 2 D-cell batteries
- 1 transparent tray
- 2 wooden blocks
- 1 can with small hole Paper towels

Section A— Performance Assessment

Inquiry 26.1 Canned Light

PROCEDURE

Read these instructions before you start working. Record your responses to A–E on Student Sheet 26.1: Section A—Performance Assessment: Canned Light.

1. Examine the flashlight.

A. Where in the flashlight is electrical energy transformed into light energy?

B. Identify the type of mirror inside the flashlight.

C. What is the purpose of this mirror?

2. Investigate what happens when you shine the flashlight into the can with the hole.

D. Record and explain your observations.

3. Keeping your finger tightly over the hole, fill the can with water.

4. Place the can next to the sink or the transparent tray, as shown in Figure 26.1.

Figure 26.1 *Shine the flashlight into the top of the can, and then remove your finger from over the hole.*

Shine the flashlight into the top of the can and remove your finger from the hole. (Make sure the water enters the tray or sink.)

E. Investigate what happens when you shine the flashlight into the can and remove your finger. Record and explain your observations.

5. Empty the water from the can and transparent tray. Be sure to mop up any spills.

6. Carefully check your responses to all questions.

Section B—Written Assessment

Your teacher will outline the procedure for taking Section B of the assessment.

Glossary

absorb: To take in and not give out again.

absorption spectrum: An electromagnetic spectrum that has been altered by passing through a substance that removes some of the passing wavelengths of light.

additive color mixing: The type of color mixing that takes place when colored lights are mixed together.

amplitude: The distance from the midpoint of a wave to the crest (or trough) of the wave.

angle of incidence: The angle at which a ray of light strikes the surface of an object, and which is measured from the normal. *See also* **normal.**

angle of reflection: The angle at which a ray of light reflects off the surface of an object and which is measured from the normal.

aperture: A hole that allows light into an optical device (such as a camera).

apparent brightness: How bright an object appears.

blind spot: The area of the retina where the optic nerve leaves the eye, which contains no light-sensitive cells and so cannot detect light.

camera: A box that produces an image by allowing light in through a hole (aperture) or lens. Usually this image is recorded on film or electronically.

Celsius: A temperature scale with a melting point of ice at 0 °C and a boiling point of water at 100 °C (at standard atmospheric pressure).

center of curvature: The point that marks the center of the sphere of which a lens surface (or surface of a curved mirror) is a part.

chemical energy: The form of energy stored in substances such as food and fuels that is transferred to other types of energy during chemical reactions, for example, when gasoline is burned.

chemical reaction: Any change (other than a nuclear reaction) that involves the formation of a new substance.

chlorophyll: A green substance found in the chloroplasts within the leaf cells of green plants. It plays an important role in photosynthesis, in which light energy is transformed to chemical energy, which is then used to make carbohydrates (food).

chloroplasts: Microscopic structures containing chlorophyll that are found in some plant cells.

chromatic aberration: A blur of colors sometimes seen around images viewed through lenses.

coherent: Waves from a source with wave troughs and peaks that are in step with one another.

color: A visual sensation produced by different wavelengths of visible light.

color filter: A transparent colored object that transmits some wavelengths of visible light while absorbing others.

component: A part of something.

cone: A type of cell found in the retina of the eye that is sensitive to certain wavelengths of light. Each of the three types of cones is sensitive to wavelengths corresponding to approximately red, green, or blue light.

cornea: A transparent outer covering at the front of the eye.

crest: The highest point of a wave. *See also* **trough.**

diffraction: The bending of waves around the edge of an obstacle.

diffraction grating: A surface (for example, a piece of plastic or glass) with closely spaced parallel lines scratched on it that produces spectra when light consisting of a mixture of wavelengths passes through it.

diffuse light source: A light source that emits light from more than one point on its surface, such as the Sun or a standard light bulb. *See also* **light source.**

diode: An electronic component, some forms of which—for example, light emitting diodes (LEDs)—can release light.

eclipse: The passage of an object through the shadow of another object. The term eclipse is usually applied to astronomical objects, for example, planets or moons.

electrical energy: The form of energy associated with electric charge and electric current.

electromagnetic radiation: Energy (contained in electric and magnetic fields) that can be transmitted without matter and may be thought of as waves or particles (photons). It includes visible light. *See also* **electromagnetic spectrum.**

electromagnetic spectrum: The range of wavelengths (from radio waves to gamma waves) over which electromagnetic radiation extends. *See also* **electromagnetic radiation.**

electron: A subatomic particle that carries a negative electrical charge.

element: A substance that cannot be broken down into other substances by chemical or physical means (except by nuclear reaction).

emission spectrum: An electromagnetic spectrum given out by a light source.

energy: The ability to make things do work.

energy transformation: The change of one form of energy into another (for example, electrical energy into light energy).

Fahrenheit: A temperature scale with a melting point of ice at 32 °F and a boiling point of water at 212 °F (at standard atmospheric pressure).

field of vision: The angle that an organism can observe with its eyes without moving its head.

filament: The part of a lightbulb that releases heat and light when an electric current is passed through it.

film: *See* **photographic film.**

focal point: The point on the principle axis of a lens or curved mirror at which rays of light from a lens or mirror come together or converge (or appear to converge).

focal length: The distance along the principle axis from the surface of a lens or mirror to the focal point.

frequency: The number of waves passing a point in a given time.

hertz: The number of waves passing a point each second.

image: A picture of an object formed by a mirror or a lens.

incident ray: A ray of light striking a surface.

infrared: Wavelengths of invisible electromagnetic radiation that are slightly longer than those of visible red light.

interference: A disturbance that may occur when waves (including light waves) travel in the same or different directions in the same space.

laser: A device that generates laser light or a laser beam. (The term "laser" is an abbreviation of Light Amplification by Stimulated Emission of Radiation.)

laser beam: *See* **laser light.**

laser diode: A diode that releases laser light. *See also* **diode.**

laser light: A monochromatic and coherent light source traveling in a thin beam. *See also* **monochromatic light.**

lens: A transparent object with at least one curved surface that can form an image when light is passed through it.

ligament: A fiber that attaches a muscle to another part of the body. Ligaments attach a ring of muscle to the lens of the eye.

light source: An object that produces light.

light year: The distance light travels through a vacuum in one year.

luminous: Producing or emitting light.

magnify: To make objects appear larger than they are.

megahertz: A unit of frequency equivalent to 1 million wavelengths per second. *See also* **hertz.**

mirror image: An image formed in a mirror. In a plane mirror, a mirror image is reversed front-to-back.

monochromatic light: Light of one wavelength.

normal: An imaginary line that is perpendicular to the surface of an object. The normal can be defined for any point on a surface. *See also* **angle of incidence; reflection; refraction.**

opaque: Not allowing any light to pass through.

optics: The study of light.

optic nerve: A bundle of nerve fibers that carries information from the eye to the brain.

optical center: The center of a lens. Light rays passing through the optical center do not change direction.

optical fiber: A transparent fiber that can transmit light by means of total internal reflection.

optical illusion: A failure of the eye to gather, or the brain to interpret, visual information correctly.

particle: The smallest amount of matter or energy of a certain type that can exist. For light, this is a photon. *See also* **photon.**

penumbra: An area of semishadow formed around the umbra that can be produced only by a diffuse or large light source.

perceive: To sense something, as in the way sense organs and the brain work together to make us aware of something. For example, the eye and the brain work together to recognize wavelengths of light, and mixtures of wavelengths, as color. The process of perceiving is called perception.

periscope: An optical device containing mirrors or prisms that is used to look over or around objects.

photographic film: A light-sensitive layer placed in a camera used for taking photographs.

photon: The smallest energy packet of light (quanta) or other electromagnetic radiation of a given wavelength that can exist.

photosynthesis: The process by which plants make food (glucose) and oxygen from water and carbon dioxide, using light as the energy source for this chemical reaction.

pinhole camera: A simple camera that admits light through a small hole without using a lens.

pixel: A small dot that makes up part of an image (for example, on a TV screen).

plane mirror: A flat mirror.

point light source: A light source that emits light from one point (or from a very small area). *See also* **light source.**

primary colors: One of three colors that can be combined to make up any desired color. For colored lights these are red, green, and blue, which are different than the primary colors used in paint or ink color mixing (cyan—blue; magenta—red; and yellow).

principle axis: An imaginary straight line that runs through the center of curvature, focal point, and the optical center of a lens (or the center of a curved mirror).

prism: A transparent object with at least two nonparallel flat sides.

quanta: The smallest packets of energy possible. Quanta of light are called photons. The singular form of quanta is "quantum."

ray: The path of light as it travels. Rays are represented as lines with arrows that show the direction in which the light travels.

real image: An image produced when light from an object is focused onto a surface. *See also* **image.**

reflect: To change the direction of a wave when it bounces off a surface.

reflected ray: A ray of light bouncing off a surface.

retina: A layer of light-sensitive cells at the back of the eye.

rod: A type of cell found in the retina of the eye that is sensitive to visible light but not to a specific color.

scatter: To absorb and then emit light in random directions.

shadow: An area of darkness that forms behind an object when the object blocks a source of light.

shutter: A movable cover over the aperture of a camera.

spectrophotometer: A device that analyzes the spectra produced by light sources or substances.

spectroscope: A device used to observe spectra.

spectroscopy: A technique used to analyze the spectra of light. Spectroscopy can be used to identify the composition of mixtures and substances.

spectrum: A distribution of colors or wavelengths of electromagnetic radiation. The plural form of spectrum is "spectra."

speed: The distance traveled in a specific time (distance divided by time).

subtractive color mixing: The type of color mixing that occurs when colors are removed (for example, by a color filter) from mixtures of light.

total internal reflection: Reflection of all the light at the boundary between two transparent substances.

translucent: Allowing light to pass through but scattering it (for example, frosted glass). *See also* **opaque; transparent.**

transmit: To allow the passage of energy or matter. For example, a red color filter transmits red light.

transparent: Allowing light of certain wavelengths to pass through without significant scattering. *See also* **opaque; translucent.**

triangular prism: A transparent object with three sides and flat ends that can be used to split white light.

trough: The lowest point of a wave. *See also* **crest.**

ultraviolet: Wavelengths of invisible electromagnetic radiation that are slightly shorter than those of visible violet light.

umbra: The inner, dark region of a shadow. No portion of the light source can be seen from within the umbra. *See also* **penumbra.**

virtual image: An image that can be seen but cannot be projected onto a screen. *See also* **image; real image.**

visible spectrum: The distribution of colors produced when white light is split.

wave: A disturbance that moves energy through matter or space without carrying matter with it.

wavelength: The distance from one wave crest to the next (also the distance from one wave trough to the next).

white light: A mixture of different colors of light that we detect as white or colorless.

Index

Photo Credits

Front Cover Harold Dorwin, Smithsonian Institution

Part 1: The Nature of Light xviii–1 Jeff McAdams, Photographer, Courtesy of Carolina Biological Supply Company 2 Exploratorium: www.exploratorium.edu 12-13 © Neal Preston/Corbis 13 © Gary Carter/ Visuals Unlimited 14 (left) Natural History Photographic Agency/© Anthony Bannister (right) Courtesy of Gary Berdeaux 15 (top left) Mark Hanna/National Optical Astronomy Observatory/Association of Universities for Research in Astronomy/National Science Foundation (top right) Agricultural Research Service/ United States Department of Agriculture (bottom left) Courtesy of the Royal Astronomical Society, London (bottom, center) Library of Congress, Prints & Photographs Division, LC-USZ62-111797 (bottom right) Library of Congress, Prints & Photographs Division, LC-USZ62-106038 16 (left) Courtesy India Tourist Office, New York (right) Asian Art Archives, University of Michigan, Ann Archor 17 English Heritage 19 (left) © Asian Art and Archaeology, Inc./Corbis (top right) Museo Nacional de Antropologia, Mexico City (bottom right) Solar and Heliospheric Observatory/ Extreme Ultraviolet Imaging Telescope Consortium 20 Corbis/Royalty-Free 27 E.R. Degginger/Color-Pic, Inc. 28 (top) Jeff McAdams, Photographer, Courtesy of Carolina Biological Supply Company (bottom) Adam Block/National Optical Astronomy Observatory/Association of Universities for Research in Astronomy/National Science Foundation 29 (top left) E.R. Degginger/Color-Pic, Inc. (top right) Courtesy of Omniglow Corporation (bottom left) Chris Corrie Photography (bottom right) Lawrence Berkeley National Laboratory 30 Doug Myerscough 31 (top) John Randall (bottom) James E. Lloyd, Department of Entomology and Nematology, University of Florida, Gainesville 32 National Aeronautics and Space Administration/Johnson Space Center 36 National Aeronautics and Space Administration/Jet Propulsion Laboratory/Voyager 2 37 (top left) Library of Congress, Prints & Photographs Division, LC-USZ62-

122699 (top right) Library of Congress, Prints & Photographs Division, LC-USZ62-124161 (bottom left) Science Museum/Science & Society Picture Library (center) Courtesy of the Archives, California Institue of Technology (right) National Academy of Sciences 39 National Optical Astronomy Observatory 40 United States Department of the Interior/National Park Service/Wind Cave National Park 48 © Rob Casey/PhotoDisc/PictureQuest 51 (top) National Oceanic and Atmospheric Administration Photo Library/Oceanic and Atmospheric Research/National Undersea Research Program (bottom) National Oceanic and Atmospheric Administration (NOAA) Photo Library/NOAA Central Library 54 © 2002 by Fred Espenak, www. MrEclipse.com 56 Photos from the private collection of Tamara Fielding and TAMARA AND THE SHADOW THEATRE OF JAVA; www.indonesianshadowplay.com 57 Photos from the private collection of Tamara Fielding and TAMARA AND THE SHADOW THEATRE OF JAVA; www.indonesianshadowplay.com 58 Jeff McAdams, Photographer, Courtesy of Carolina Biological Supply Company 64-65 Courtesy of George Eastman House 66-67 Courtesy Walpole Gallery, London 67 (top) Gernsheim Collection, Harry Ransom Humanities Research Center, The University of Texas at Austin (bottom) Kent Knudson/ Photo Link/PhotoDisc/PictureQuest 68 Corbis/Royalty-Free 70 (top) Photographic History Collection, National Museum of American History, Smithsonian Institution (center left) National Geophysical Data Center (right) Corbis/Royalty-Free (bottom left) Corbis/Royalty-Free 78 © RDF/Visuals Unlimited 79 (top) National Oceanic and Atmospheric Administration (NOAA) Photo Library/NOAA Central Library (bottom) Corbis/Royalty-Free 80 (top) MSCUA, University of Washington Libraries, Farquharson 4, 12 (bottom) MSCUA, University of Washington Libraries, Farquharson 4, 12 81 The National Symphony Orchestra, Leonard Slatkin, Music Director. Photographer Margot I. Shulman 82 Corbis/Royalty-Free 87 (top) © M.J.F. Marsland 2000 (bottom) Courtesy of

Carolina Biological Supply Company **89** Northwind Picture Archives **90** Corbis Images, PictureQuest **91** © David Marsland **92** Jeff McAdams, Photographer, Courtesy of Carolina Biological Supply Company **99** Infrared Processing and Analysis Center, Caltech **100** National Museum of Photography, Film & Television/Science & Society Picture Library **102** Infrared Processing and Analysis Center, Caltech/ Jet Propulsion Laboratory **103 (top)** Instituto Nacional de Pesquisas Espaciais **(center)** National Climate Data Center/National Oceanic and Atmospheric Administration **(bottom)** Visuals Unlimited **104 (top left)** National Aeronautics and Space Administration and C.R. O'Dell (Rice University) **(top right)** National Aeronautics and Space Administration and R. Thompson (University of Arizona) **(bottom)** Courtesy of National Renewable Energy Laboratory/United States Department of Energy **105** Stockbyte/PictureQuest **106 (left)** Corbis Images/PictureQuest **(center)** Guido Alberto Rossi/Brand X Pictures/PictureQuest **(right)** Corbis/Royalty-Free **107 (top)** National Aeronautics and Space Administration/Goddard Space Flight Center: Total Ozone Mapping Spectrometer **(bottom left)** National Cancer Institute **(bottom right)** Corbis/ Royalty-Free **108** Courtesy of David Marsland/ © NSRC **114** © Association of Universities for Research in Astronomy, Inc. (AURA), All Rights Reserved **115 (top)** http://imagine.gsfc.nasa.gov **(bottom left)** National Aeronautics and Space Administration/Jet Propulsion Laboratory/Caltech **(bottom right)** Climate Monitoring and Diagnostics Lab/ Atmospheric Research Observatory/National Oceanic and Atmospheric Administration **116** Bruce Fritz, Agricultural Research Service/United States Department of Agriculture **121** Eric Long, Smithsonian Institution **123 (top)** Northwind Picture Archives **(bottom)** © 1997, The British Library Board **124 (left)** *The Clip Art Book,* Crescent Books, Avenel, New Jersey, 1994 **(right)** Library of Congress, Prints & Photographs Division, LC-USZ62-104244 **(bottom)** Courtesy of the Library of Congress **125** From the collection of Mill Grove—Audubon Wildlife Sanctuary **126** Photography by Ferne Saltzman, Official Balloon Fiesta® Photographer, © Albuquerque International Balloon Fiesta Inc. **128-129** Visuals Unlimited **130** © Joe McDonald/Visuals Unlimited **131** © Thomas Cida/Visuals Unlimited **132** © Michael Pole/Corbis **135** National Library of Medicine, National Institutes of Health **138** Jeff McAdams, Photographer, Courtesy of Carolina Biological Supply Company

Part 2: Reflection and Refraction **142-143** Eric Long, Smithsonian Institution **144** © Audrey Gilson/Visuals Unlimited **146 (top)** © David Marsland **(bottom)** 3M™ Scotchlite™ Reflective Material 3M and Scotchlite are trademarks of 3M company **147** Corbis/ Royalty-Free **151 (all)** © David Marsland **152** © Historical Pictures Archive/Corbis **(bottom)** University of Pennsylvania Museum **153 (top)** Binswanger Mirror **(bottom left)** Plate with border of grotesques on an orange ground; in the center, Narcissus gazing at his reflection in a fountain, Widener Collection, Photograph © 2002 Board of Trustees, National Gallery of Art, Washington **(bottom right)** Illustration by John Tenniel **154** National Archives and Records Administration **159** E.R. Degginger/Color-Pic, Inc. **164** National Oceanic and Atmospheric Administration (NOAA) Photo Library/NOAA Central Library **165** Private Donor **166** National Aeronautics and Space Administration/Photograph by Charles Conrad Jr. **168** © Gary Hodson/Visuals Unlimited **170** E.R. Degginger/Color-Pic, Inc. **173** Allenbeys.com, Inc. **174** E.R. Degginger/Color-Pic, Inc. **175 (top)** National Archives and Records Administration **(bottom)** National Archives and Records Administration **176** National Archives and Records Administration **177 (top left)** © David Marsland **(top right)** E.R. Degginger/Color-Pic, Inc. **(center right)** Jeff McAdams, Photographer, Courtesy of Carolina Biological Supply Company **(bottom)** National Radio Astronomy Observatory/Associated Universities, Inc. **178-179** National Aeronautics and Space Administra-